M000208446

NEW MOON RISING

NEW MOON RISING

RECLAIMING THE SACRED
RITES OF MENSTRUATION

Linda Heron Wind

DELPHI PRESS, INC.
CHICAGO, ILLINOIS

delphi press

© 1995 by Linda Heron Wind
Published 1995 by Delphi Press, Inc., Chicago, Illinois.
All rights reserved.

No part of this book may be reproduced in any form, except for brief quotations accompanying reviews in newspapers or magazines without the prior written consent of the publisher.

ISBN 1-878980-12-2

Library of Congress Catalogue Number: 93-73574

Acknowledgements

Grateful acknowledgement is given for permission to reproduce the words and music of the songs included in this book:

Sue Kalchik St. Pierre, *A New Moon is Rising*, *Our Sacred Tears*, and *Sisters of Our Moon*; Ani Williams, *She*; Brooke Medicine Eagle, *I Walk a Path of Beauty* and *I Give Away Blood of Life*; Rashani, *Pueo*; Elaine Peterson, *Moon Song*; Marsha L. Meuse, *Vision Beauty Song*.

Grateful acknowldgement is also given to Ballantine Books for permission to include an except from *One Is the Sun* by Patricia Nell Warren, © 1991 by Patricia Nell Warren.

Contents

Acknowledgments

I am most grateful to Grandmother Spotted Eagle for the discipline and guidance she gave to the writing of this book. Her presence was my motivation.

I give thanks to my sister and friend, Annette Margaret, for awakening me to the value of the feminine, for sharing my journey, and for her many words of encouragement.

For her teachings which speak to my heart and her friendship and support, I thank Brooke Medicine Eagle.

To my Eagle Song sisters who are a constant source of inspiration for me as we weave our rainbow web of love and dance the flower song, thank you.

I thank the women of the Rainbow Chrysalis Lodge for all you have taught me about the strength of women in community. I also thank my women friends, clients and students who continue to teach me about courage and beauty.

For my spouse equivalent, Paul Hyland, thank you for supporting my journey.

I thank my mother, Jean Anderson, for all she taught me about caring and my father, Ted Anderson, for his constant belief in me. I also thank my son, Richard Pinckney, for the joy of his being and the beauty of his balance.

I am grateful to my colleagues for their support of my work.

Much thanks goes to Karen Jackson of Delphi Press for her enthusiastic response to this book and her diligent work in bringing it into its final form. Also thanks to my friends who helped, Eileen Garwood for getting the songs onto paper and Carol Buck for my photograph.

And a final thanks to Tigger Wabun Wind for her love and companionship always, but especially during the writing of this book.

Dedication

This book is dedicated to the Grandmothers of yesterday, today and tomorrow, that they may carry the teachings forth to the children and thus, restore balance to the peoples of the Earth.

Introduction

The time has come for the voice of women's experience to be heard. It is the voice which values relationship and connection to all things in the circle of life. This voice comes from the deepest parts of our beings, those parts that know Earth as Mother, Moon as Grandmother, and the plants and animals as our brothers and sisters. It speaks to all women as our sisters and to all men as our brothers, and it calls us to re-member our wholeness and our holiness.

The voice of women's experience speaks through this book—voices from the past, from the present, and from the future—calling women everywhere to honor their heritage and their birthright. While this book focuses on honoring the menstrual cycle, at the same time it teaches us to see ourselves as women of value and power who have much wisdom to offer a world which desperately needs our vision. It calls us to claim our power, to become warriors who stand firm in our centers and in our truth. As we reclaim our menstrual rites (and rights), we discover who we really are as women.

To the women who read these words and feel them in their bellies, welcome to the dance.

1

To the Men Who Read This Book

While this book focuses on menstruation, which is uniquely a woman's experience, the feminine values of which it speaks live within men as well. May it call you to find and honor the feminine within you and inspire you to explore the question of what it means to be a man. Women become warriors when they honor their feminine and bring their dreams and visions into reality by also developing their masculine side. Men are true warriors when their creative masculine energy is guided by the feminine within them. It is the feminine within both men and women which connects us to each other and all of life and brings us dreams of peace and love. It is the masculine which makes those dreams real in the world.

The use of the word "patriarchy" in this book should not be interpreted as "men." Patriarchy is a social, political, and economic system which has devalued women and robbed men of their wholeness. It is practiced by men and women alike. As we walk our individual paths back to balance, women and men need to walk side by side, each with their unique gifts to offer, with respect and value for each other.

1

Women's Wisdom Over Time

Moon Talk

"But Grandmother, I don't understand!"

"Ah, my daughter, let me first explain that there are two kinds of understanding—understanding with the mind and understanding with the heart. I can help you to understand with your mind, but understanding with your heart will only come from inside of you when you have begun to experience these things for yourself.

"It is important to begin with the understanding that men and women have different gifts, different gifts that are equal in value. Women carry within them a womb which is the place where all new life is created and nurtured. It is also the symbol of all creation, the womb of the Earth from which all physical things are born. So one gift that women have is the gift of the womb and the creativity and nurturing it symbolizes. Another related gift is the life giving blood that flows each lunar cycle. This blood can physically nurture our own children growing inside us or it can nurture the plants in our garden. But more than that, it provides a time for release and renewal, for connecting with Earth and her children,

5

for connecting with the spirit that moves in all things, for connecting with our own inner knowing, the knowing of all women. A powerful time, wouldn't you say?"

"Is that why mother does different things while she's bleeding?"

"It is good for a woman to honor her bleeding time, to make the best use of such a powerful time. Women for many thousands of years have looked to Grandmother Moon for guidance in these matters, just as you, my little one, have come to a grandmother for wisdom. Grandmother Moon teaches us that there are times when we shine brightly and are very active but as we grow closer to our bleeding time we come back into ourselves, just as she covers her face to the rest of the world at the time of the new Moon.

"As women, bleeding gives us the gift of the cycle of renewal. With the waning Moon, we let go of the world and prepare to let go of our blood to renew our wombs and ourselves for new life, new ways of being. With the waxing Moon, we draw the wisdom gained from this experience back into our daily lives.

"When women come into their Moontime, their bleeding, their hearts become open to knowing the truths of women, the truths of the universe. As they withdraw from the external world and look inward, they see their gifts, they know their path, they see vision for their community, for their people. This knowledge is most valuable for maintaining harmony among all the beings of Earth. Moontime is a very sacred gift and a very powerful time."

"Grandmother, do all women know these things?"

"Yes, Dawn, I am happy to say that now they do. All women know the power and correct use of their Moontime and, I might add, all men honor these gifts of women.

"But it was not always so. There was a time that spanned several thousand years when there was a great deal of struggle between men and women over whose gifts were greater. While this did not involve all the peoples of Earth, it did affect many greatly. During this time it appeared that men wanted more power than women and found many ways to get it. Men have a gift of physical strength and, rather than using this strength for the good of the community,

6

they began to use it to have power over women and children and even other peoples. Men no longer allowed women to have an equal voice in the community decision making and even called them witches and killed them when they practiced traditional healing, especially healing for women in childbirth. It seemed that men wanted control of healing too. This continued for a long time and, although many women tried to honor their gifts secretly, many more women began to believe that their gifts were not as important as men's. Some even forgot they had gifts! Some even believed the myths that made women the source of all evil in the world.

"After quite some time, things began to change. Some women began to question why men should be superior to women when men and women could do most of the same things. They suggested that only men's physical strength was superior and that didn't even happen to be all that important in society at that time. So they began to fight for women's equality and in doing so, won back much power in the form of laws which protected women from abuse of men's power and allowed women access to compete with men within the society which men had created.

"There was something missing, however. Women's gifts were still not being honored. The most valuable gifts of creation, nurturing, inner knowing, and cycles of renewal were not highly valued by men and, sadly enough, they were often not valued by women either. Some women had been so busy competing with men to prove they were equal that they had tried to pretend their own gifts didn't exist, perhaps because it would make them different and provide a reason for them to be discriminated against. Needless to say, the combination of men wanting to assume power over women, women competing with men for this power, and the absence of honor for women's gifts led to considerable disharmony at that time. Even the smallest pebble on the beach was touched by those vibrations.

"As women found success in competing with men, they began to have this nagging feeling that something was missing. Sometimes this was more than a feeling. Women suffered a great deal

7

from the disharmony this struggle created within them. Depression, stress, anxiety, illness were only a few of the problems which resulted. But through experiencing these problems and women's natural ability of looking inward, women began to put their finger on the underlying reality. Their gifts were needed by the people to restore balance on Earth. They saw how not honoring their natural cycles had created much stress. To maintain the appearance of linear function while your body is undergoing a cycle is quite difficult. It is like trying to stay awake while you are being called to sleep and dream. A very irritating experience! And to be so in touch with your inner knowing about nurturing, renewal, and respect for all life when you look outside you and see abuse, disrespect for life, children starving, and power games with the man in your life or in your career was truly a schizophrenic experience. It is a wonder that women survived these times and remained sane. Even the medical profession of the time told women that they were abnormal for being irritated and angry, depressed and emotional before their bleeding. They called the disorder PMS. Fancy words do not explain what was happening for these women. But perhaps the discomfort they experienced pushed them to look for the real issues and opened them up to their own experience.

"It took some time but gradually women began to know their gifts and to understand that they are not only as valuable as men's gifts, but it is necessary for women to use those gifts to create a balanced and harmonious world.

"Grandmother, how lucky I am to be born in this time when women know the power of their blood!"

"Ah, perhaps it was also you who helped with the struggle back then, and perhaps you remember also that time of honor long ago. Who knows? But, yes, you are lucky and should be grateful to all those women who paved the way for this time and also to the men who have gone through many struggles and much suffering to relearn harmonious ways to use their gifts.

"Let's begin, then, with your learning. You are now preparing to take your place in the world as a woman. As you can see from our look back over time, there is much responsibility in assuming that role. The harmony of the community and the welfare of the children will depend on you. There is much to learn. Let me sing you a song now that was written by a woman at the time when honoring the power and responsibility of Moon blood was beginning to come back. She wrote this song for all her sisters and the generations to come to help them remember."

"Did you know her Grandmother?"

"Yes, I did. And you will also know her through this song:

A new Moon is rising, silver sliver in a Moonlit sky.
A new Moon is rising, Grandmother's watchful eye.
A new Moon is rising, pulling great ocean tides.
A new Moon is rising, swelling up, swelling up inside.
Blood of the earth, blood of my veins
Feel it flowing, sweetwater flowing, sweetwater
    flowing
Blood of the earth, blood of my veins
Feel it flowing, in the womb flowing, sweetwater
    flowing.
Gentle woman, please claim your power
Gentle woman, creation's power
To nurture, to heal, to teach
To nurture, to heal, to teach
That the blood of the violent wounds will stop
They're killing the children, killing the children, killing
    the children
That the blood of the womb will be cherished, every
    drop
Create for the children, create for the children, create
    for the children
Oh gentle woman, please claim your power
Gentle woman, creation's power
Gentle woman, please claim your power.
A new Moon is rising, pure light in the darkest night.
A new Moon is rising, gentle power wielding such
    might.

A new Moon is rising, pulling great ocean tides.
A new Moon is rising, swelling up, swelling up inside.
Blood of the earth, blood of my veins
Feel it flowing, sweetwater flowing, sweetwater
    flowing
Blood of the earth, blood of my veins
In the womb flowing, sweetwater flowing, sweetwater
    flowing, sweetwater flowing...."[1]

Grandmother, a wise woman of the future, knows the long history of differing views on menstruation. Looking back at how menstruation has been viewed in other cultures and over time, gives us a clearer perspective on where we stand today. It also gives us some choices as we view ourselves as women having connections over time and culture to other women and to a wisdom of our own.

With the increasing interest in women's issues over recent years, historians and anthropologists have taken a new look at what we used to call "primitive" cultures, societies such as Native American, Australian aboriginal, African, and some very early Scandinavian and European peoples. One of their interesting findings is that, before contact with Western civilization, many of these native cultures were fairly balanced in power between men and women, with some leaning in a more woman-centered direction. These people seemed also to be more in tune with the rhythm of the Earth's natural cycles and to live in balance with the animals and plants. It is interesting to look at how life was different for women in cultures where they were perceived as equal to men in power, yet different in attributes and characteristics.

Archaeological accounts indicate that a matrilineal clan system can be traced from the Neolithic age and that the shift to a patrilineal system occurred at different points in different parts of the world.

Among the Mediterranean cultures, Greek civilization was the beginning of the revolution to a patrilineal system, while in parts of the British Isles matrilineal succession existed until the ninth century and it continues through the present time among some Native Americans and other indigenous peoples. The word "matrimony" which originally referred to inheritance of property in the maternal line came to mean marriage because marriage was the way for a man to control the property of the woman he was marrying. The spread of Christianity and the invasion of European Christians was the primary source of the change to patriarchy in many areas of the world, including Europe, Scandinavia, Africa, and the Americas. Thus, the patriarchal system in which we now live is a relatively recent event in the long history of humanity.[2]

We do know that in these older matrilineal systems going back to the earliest human cultures menstrual blood was considered sacred. It gave rise to many creation stories where the universe and all that is in it came from the Moon blood of the Great Mother Goddess.[3] The name "Adam" comes from a feminine word which means "bloody clay."[4] The Koran's creation story as well says that man was made by Allah out of flowing blood. In pre-Islamic Arabia Allah was the Goddess of creation, Allat.[5] Barbara Walker traces the reverence of menstrual blood as being sacred and symbolizing wisdom through every culture in the world showing its primary significance within matrilineal cultures. All of the first calendars were based on the 13 lunar months, the 28 day cycle of both women and the Moon. Walker relates the decline of women's power and the subsequent negative view of menstruation which we are left with today, to the fact that the blood represented women's power and thus it had to be denigrated. "Because menstrual blood occupied a central position in matriarchal theologies.... patriarchal-ascetic thinkers showed almost hysterical fear of it."[6] It was thought that a man might be killed, lose his eyesight or strength if he walked near a menstruating woman. The very substance which was used in fertility rites in planting and raising crops in matrilineal systems, was seen as polluting and able to damage crops in a patrilineal system.

After the Enlightenment when science replaced symbolic magic, and science was of course called upon to continue the repression. Nineteenth-century doctors carried on this tradition and maintained that menstruating women were not healthy. A condition called neurasthenia, consisting of symptoms of blushing, vertigo, headaches, insomnia, depression, and uterine irritability, was said to be caused by the strain on an already "weak" female reproductive system. This weakness was further strained by women's ambition and intellectual activity. Physicians thought that mental breakdown would occur when women attempted to compete with men rather than serving them.[7]

Things have not improved much in our century—just consider the current medicalization of women's natural functions of menstruation, childbirth, and menopause that has grown out of this historical suppression of women. Even while we believe that we, as women, have made great strides in achieving equality, the diagnosis of "late luteal phase disphoric disorder" has been placed in the latest revision of the Diagnostic and Statistical Manual of the American Psychiatric Association, labeling premenstrual symptoms as a mental disorder. It seems odd that symptoms which are experienced by up to 80% of women in our culture as part of a natural cycle would be labeled a "disorder." Katherine Dalton, a British physician and author of a book on PMS, suggests that over half of all women suffer from PMS and it is their "duty" to be treated (she pushed progesterone therapy) "otherwise they will get what they deserve from men."[8] Another recent book on PMS describes the disorder as "a defect of physiology, not of character" and as "a complex disorder linked to the cyclic activity of the hypothalamic-pituitary-ovarian axis."[9] As recently as 1990 an article in an obstretical and gynecological journal reported on hysterectomies and removal of the ovaries as a treatment for severe premenstrual syndrome.[10]

This insistence upon medical intervention in natural functioning is particularly astonishing in the light of recent cross-cultural studies of menstruation. Anthropologists find that PMS symptoms are not universal—that is, there are many cultures where PMS appears to be non-existent.[11] This seriously questions the current physical approaches to PMS.

Most women born and raised in post World War II America have been led to believe that their reproductive functions are abnormal and require treatment. In addition to all of the drug treatments and surgery for menstrual "abnormalities," 25% of all births in America are caesarean sections. Most "normal" births require spending hours on our backs—a position which even doctors admit make the birth more difficult for the woman.[12] Until recently, women squatted to give birth, a much easier position for pushing, but more difficult for the doctor to see and control what is going on. (After all, who is more important in the process?)

The medical establishment now has women believing that horrible things will happen to them if they do not take hormones at menopause. For millennia women have looked forward to this time of holding their blood and their wisdom. Suddenly we need to be medicated to survive it? Even though the World Health Organization recently stated that fewer than 20% of women experience symptoms of menopause that might require hormonal treatment, physicians continue to recommend hormones to women with scare tactics and the literature of drug companies continues to portray menopausal women without hormones as not acceptable in our society.[13] I listen with horror when I hear fairly young women who have had hysterectomies say, "The problem wasn't too serious, but I told the doctor to take it all out. I don't need it any more." This is the extent to which we have been brain-washed.

If we look back in time, we see that women's unique ability to bring forth life into the world was honored. One could say that the greater respect paid to women was because a greater number of children meant more future workers in the community. However, the ability to give birth was also seen as a natural cycle patterned after the many cycles of the "first mother," Mother Earth. The concept of mother was also much broader than the way in which we think about it today. To accept the role of mother meant to be a keeper of good relationship, to make sure the community and its leaders nurtured their people, and to make good decisions which would affect generations to come.

The menstrual cycle was treated as a sacred event, a natural cycle of renewal. The cycle length is the same as that of the Moon waxing and waning from changing from new Moon to full Moon to new Moon (28 days), and many natives cultures felt that if a woman was outside and her eyes exposed to the light of the Moon on a regular basis, ovulation would occur on the full Moon and menstruation on the new Moon.[14] It is interesting to note that research supports this notion of a woman cycling with the Moon and suggests that a woman's cycle can be regulated by exposure to the full Moon at night.[15] Thus, a woman's menstrual period was referred to as "Moontime." "Grandmother Moon" was also thought to play an important role in teaching women how they were to move with their cycle. At the approach of the new Moon, or a woman's Moontime, Grandmother Moon covers her face and does not involve herself in the world. Opposite Moontime, on the full Moon which normally coincides with ovulation, she shines brightly and is very active.

Native women all over the world in many different cultures made use of the menstrual hut or Moon Lodge.[16] While its exact use was governed by the customs of a particular culture, in general, the Moon Lodge was a place where a woman could go just before and during the first few days of her period or Moontime to be by herself or in the company of other women. Here she could nurture herself, meditate, and not be interrupted by her normal everyday activities. The grandmothers and men took care of children, cooked meals, and did the other chores of the menstruating woman. Moontime was seen by men and women alike as a sacred and powerful time to be spent seeking vision, growth, and creativity. A woman was thought to be most powerful in her receptive ability during Moontime, receptive to the energy of others and to communication with Spirit. To stay around the energy of other people at that time was not considered good use of this receptive power. Through retreat and meditation, however, her intuitions and visions could benefit the whole community. Some of the visions of the future predicted by the Hopi—of trains, telephone wires, road ways, and airplanes—came from women in Moon Lodges.[17]

Ruby Modesto, a Cahuilla medicine woman, pointed out how women viewed the importance of this retreat:

> The women didn't feel that they were being imposed upon when they retired to the menstrual hut. They got to be by themselves for three or four days. It was a ceremonial occasion which enabled a woman to get in touch with her own special power. It was a time to Dream and have visions. Each month the women went to their own vision pit. The men had vision pits too, places to dream and pray... This was how the people learned.[18]

It is interesting to note that the early white male anthropologists observing this practice interpreted "confinement" in the Moon lodge as isolation of the woman so she would not contaminate food she prepared or the men of the tribe. Since she did not participate in community ceremony at that time, it was seen as further evidence of her ability to contaminate. In fact, these conclusions were, in some cases, reflections of the anthropologists views of menstruation in the white, male-dominant culture (in which menstruation and pain in childbirth are the curse of Eve), and are quite opposite of what was believed by the natives. It is not unusual for the menstrual practices of a culture to be described as "taboos." The word taboo means forbidden but it also means sacred, something that is forbidden to be touched or discussed lightly less its sacredness be profaned. Thus taboos were not likely to be talked about to outsiders, particularly by women to men. While the menstrual taboos of a culture are often described by men in terms of contamination, women sometimes describe the same practice in positive terms, suggesting that the contamination ideas symbolize fear of women's power. Anthropologists discuss the wide variation in meaning of menstrual taboos among cultures suggesting that, "Many menstrual taboos, rather than protecting society from a universally ascribed feminine evil, explicitly protect the perceived creative spirituality of menstruous women from the influence of others in a more neutral state, as well as protecting the latter in turn from the potent positive spiritual force ascribed to such women."[19] It is true that in many cultures women did not participate in ceremony during their menses but it was because menstruating women were seen as more powerful than the medicine person or shaman at that time and this power would disrupt the shaman's ability to carry out the ceremony. A better use for this power would be in the Moon Lodge where the receptivity of the woman could be used for the good of the community. These practices are still followed today by some Native American peoples. Mona, a Hopi woman, speaks of menstruation:

> When a woman is in the fullness of her Moon... it is important for her to create inner space for herself. It is her true time of growth, of purification, and of keen introspection. It is also the time of her greatest power. That is why a woman does not participate in the ceremonies during her Moon time. In such times when each individual is using his or her own personal power to purify and heal ... the intense focus of power in the menstruating woman can overwhelm others. So she goes off, perhaps with other women who are also menstruating, to create experiences that are important to her. Then she rejoins the other members of the community in the 'Talking Circle' ceremony and shares what she has gained in her time of separation.[20]

Mona's husband, Nelson, indicated that he "recognizes this time as a wonderful aspect of his wife's being. Periods of emotionalism and crying are regarded as valuable and even crucial transitions for both men and women. Nelson explained that in order to be a full man, a real warrior, the man must be in touch with his feminine aspects. He talked about the feminine qualities as being in touch with loving, giving, nurturing, the experience of connectedness, the Mother Earth."[21]

In looking at other native cultures around the world, there are many different views of menstruation, suggesting that, in part, the view is shaped by the culture. There is, however, almost universal significance given to menstruation through taboos. Among the Beng of the Ivory Coast in Africa, menstrual blood is seen as the symbol of human fertility. A male informant said, "Menstrual blood is special because it carries in it a living being. It works like a tree. Before bearing fruit, a tree must first bear flowers. Menstrual blood is like

16

the flower: it must emerge before the fruit—the baby—can be born."[22]

Among the Aboriginal people of Australia, men have ritual ceremonies in which they imitate menstruation and childbirth, suggesting men's desire to have the power of a menstruating woman.[23]

Another glaring difference between these earlier cultures and our own present culture is how they inform girls about their menstrual cycles. In more woman-honoring cultures, girls approaching their first Moontime did so with great anticipation. This event would mark entrance into womanhood and the beginning of her Moon Lodge visits. There was much celebration in the whole community and a ceremony, which in one tribe was called, "Her alone they sing over."[24] She would be given presents, have a special dress, be given a name that represented her unique gifts, and have her face painted to signify her womanhood. Before this time she would have been taught by the grandmothers and other women of the tribe what her responsibilities were as a woman—what it meant to be a woman. She was told that she was to live in a way that would maintain good relationship within the community and to be a nurturer of all life. While all girls were taught to cook, sew, and tend children, in many tribes a woman could choose to be a hunter and protector of the people just as a man could choose to cook and sew. This was not often the case but such role reversal tended to be accepted when it occurred.

So a young girl approaching womanhood had clear positive expectations and was proud to be a woman. Because of the equality of power, men respected women. There was no rape, child abuse, or wife beating in these cultures. These would be such shameful acts that the perpetrator would be expelled from the community. In some tribes a woman who was dissatisfied with the way her husband was treating her needed only to put his clothes on the doorstep. Quick and easy divorce, but not done without good reason.

In contrast to this positive approach is the lack of initiation into womanhood which occurs in our culture. In *The Curse: A Cultural History of Menstruation,* Janice Delaney, Mary Jane Lupton and

Emily Toth comment on how our culture reacts to the onset of menstruation:

> We live in a greeting card culture where, for twenty five cents, we purchase socially approved statements about childbirth, marriage, or death. But Hallmark manufactures no cards that say, 'Best Wishes on Becoming A Woman.' Rather than celebrate the coming-of-age in America we hide the fact of menarche, just as we are advised to deodorize, sanitize, and remove the evidence.[25]

They also point out that this taboo of silence on menstruation in our culture is most evident in restrictions placed on advertisement for sanitary protection products. There are oblique references to absorbency and cleanliness but none to anatomy, comfort, insertion, application, duration, efficiency—or blood. In a study of college women's recollection of menarche, it was reported that, while most said they had received some information about the biology of menstruation prior to menarche, the women felt they had not been prepared for the event on a personal level.[26] Other studies also indicate that premenstrual girls have the most negative attitudes about menstruation, expecting to experience more pain and discomfort than post-menarcheal girls.[27] They also found more negative experiences with menstruation in girls who were poorly prepared and that this negative experience continued even after menstruating for several years. The research in this area is clear that, while we have made strides in simply informing girls about menstruation prior to menarche, there is very little preparation for or recognition of the event. If menstruation is in any way symbolic of women's power, then our culture has a taboo not only on preparing young women to assume their power but on even talking about women's power.

As a woman grew to the end of her childbearing years, and passed into menopause, or Moonpause, she was considered to hold her power. She was inducted into the grandmother lodge, the council of white-haired women, the wise ones.[28] She then took up the responsibility of teaching the young children and serving as council to the community. Highly respected for her wisdom, she was sought out by the younger men and women when there were problems. She took an active role in the spiritual life of the community, by arranging for and actively participating in ceremonies. Most importantly she became the advocate for good relationship within the community and with all relations in the circle of life—all Earth's children, human, plants and animals. As you might guess, women looked forward to entering the grandmother lodge at the beginning of menopause. It was a time to begin sharing the wisdom one inevitably gains from living and participating fully in the life of the community.

Another contrast between these more ancient views and the practices of our modern culture is that ancient cultures celebrated rites of passage which are linked to our natural cycle of growth. This is the case with the young woman who has her first menstrual period as well as with a woman going through menopause. Because of the way in which our society views menstruation, these wonderful events have become something to hide, if not to fear. Part of this results from unequal value assigned to being male or female in our society. This is evident from the use of the male model as normal functioning for everything from medical wellness to psychologically healthy characteristics. For example, if we look at the characteristics typically defined as masculine or feminine, such as active/passive, strong/weak, logical/emotional, we can see that those associated with the masculine are all desirable in our society and those associated with the feminine are not.

For a while it was suggested that the ideal for men and women alike was to have both male and female characteristics, that is to be androgynous.[29] However, it became clear that for a woman, being androgynous had advantages in our culture while for a man, there was no advantage of adopting the feminine characteristics. It is still the male characteristics alone which predict higher self-esteem.[30]

Likewise, from a male model, hormones seem to provide more of a steady state, which is seen as desirable, while the hormones of women fluctuate on a monthly cycle. The mood swings and associated changes created by this cycle are then considered "not normal" and something which must be regulated because they do not follow the male, steady-state pattern. Most women who are trying to succeed in the male environment of the working world try their best to hide their natural cycle, particularly the emotional shifts which accompany it—hiding so that the typical negative labels will not be applied to them, so that anything they do at that time won't be attributed to their being premenstrual or "on the rag."

Men alone are not to blame for this situation. We have all grown up in a culture which does not value the feminine or women. Men's attitudes are often reflections of women's attitudes about themselves. In older, more balanced cultures, women were taught from an early age to honor the special qualities that defined their womanhood. They were proud to be women. Men also valued the qualities women had and were taught to honor their feminine side. One tragic observation of our own culture is that the far majority of girls, when asked if they are happy to be girls, express a wish that they could have been boys. It is rare, indeed, to find a boy who wishes he could have been a girl. That tells us something about the values being communicated to our children, girls and boys alike. When economic, political, medical, technological, religious, and psychological power is in the hands of men, or women who emulate men, it is difficult for women to know what is "normal," as only half the human experience is viewed as valuable—and it is not our half! The entire culture loses because it is not whole or healthy unless it values the feminine and nurturing. Many of the problems our society is faced with today are the direct result of lack of nurturing—of our children, of the land, of the animals, of the trees, of ourselves, of each other.

It is time for women to begin to honor ourselves as women. A good place to begin is by honoring our natural cycle, the menstrual cycle, our Moontime. In beginning this process it is important to look carefully at your cycle of changes throughout the month in a non-judgmental way. Take the time to be aware of not only how you feel but why you are feeling that way. It is certainly easier to attribute emotions of anger, hopelessness, sadness, and irritability to PMS, or our hormones, than to look for what our bodies are trying to tell us about the environment we live in or what changes we need to make in ourselves. It is true that the hormone balances change just prior to menstruation, but recent research suggests that the function of that change may be to move us more into our right brains—the emotional, intuitive, creative and feminine side of our brain. If this means that we are more in touch with what it means to be a woman, our nurturing of all life, then it also very likely means that we are going to come into greater conflict with the world around us which does not honor that nurturing. That could certainly make us angry, hopeless, sad and irritable. Making use of this time of openness to change for growth and inner work would honor this natural cycle.

One way of beginning the process of getting in touch with ourselves is to set aside time to relax and be quiet. If this is practiced on a regular basis, it becomes much easier to quiet ourselves and go within to find our own knowing about our bodies and emotions at the time when we need to do that the most. Women researchers currently studying PMS have chosen to re-label the time as PMA—Premenstrual Awareness.[31] No one knows better than you do what is going on in your life or what your body is saying to you. Relaxation and quieting is one way of listening to our bodies, to ourselves, in order to become aware of our own knowing. If we do not listen, but try to cover up, ignore, put up with the "symptoms," our bodies will only speak louder. Once a month we have the opportunity to become more aware, more in tune with our bodies. We have a time to see what there is in our environment which is inconsistent with what we intuitively know to be right. Through exploring new ways of looking at who we are as women and honoring the changes of the menstrual cycle, perhaps we can reclaim some of the wisdom of those native women who have gone before us, our tribal ancestors, and bring it back to enrich our present lives and culture and to restore balance within ourselves and our world.

2

Honoring Our Cycle

Roots and Wind

Grandmother and Dawn walked through the meadow toward the big old tree which stood at the edge of the woods.

"Look at how tall she is Grandmother! She must be very old."

"She is very old, probably a sapling when my great, great grandmother walked this land. Can you imagine how much she has seen and how much she knows?"

"That is even hard to think about."

"Let's give her a big hug. Put your arms around her and press your body to her and close your eyes. Do you feel her sap running under the bark?"

"I'm not sure what that feels like, but it makes me feel good all over."

"That's good. It's important to learn from the trees, especially the old ones like this one who have so much knowledge to share. Let's sit down here and lean against her trunk and see if we can soak up a little of her wisdom."

"Her trunk feels good on my back too."

"One of the things that trees teach us is how important it is to have roots which extend deep into the Earth. Not only do these roots hold us upright but they bring us nourishment."

"But Grandmother, we don't have roots like a tree, we move around."

"That is true, Dawn, but the tree's roots are a symbol for things we need in our lives to be stable. If we think of what the tree's roots do for it and then look at how we meet those needs in our life, we will be learning the wisdom of the tree as a symbol for how we should live. What is one thing that the tree's roots do for it?"

"Well, I guess the most obvious is that it connects the tree firmly to the Earth Mother to keep it from falling over in the wind"

"Yes, and what connects us to the Earth Mother and keeps us from falling over in the wind?"

"I feel connected to the Earth when I walk in the meadow with the flowers and sit with the trees but I don't think that would keep me from falling over in the wind unless I was hanging on to a tree!"

"Good. It is true that being with the flowers and trees reminds us of our connection. The wind is a symbol for change and things which happen in our lives which create change. So not being blown over by the wind means not being thrown off balance by change."

"Oh, I understand now. You mean like the time when the fire burned our home and I lost some of my favorite things and we had no place to stay. That certainly changed my life! I remember that Mom got us up to watch the sun rise the next morning. We stood on the hill watching the golden sky at dawn and gave thanks that we were all together and safe. I felt more peaceful seeing the sun come up but I'm not sure why."

"Perhaps it is because being in nature reminds us that things move in cycles. The sun rises each day and then it sets, bringing darkness, only to rise again the next day, bringing back the light. So we move in our lives, with cycles of light and dark. The sun's rising each day tells us that we should not fear being lost in the darkness, that it will not last forever."

"Yes, I felt hopeful when I saw the sun rise."

"Our roots, then, are in nature and its cycles. If we touch into those cycles and know that they are a part of us, it keeps us from being blown over in the winds of change."

"Wow, I never thought about it like that before. A woman's Moon cycle must be like that too."

"Yes, for a woman the cycles of renewal move through her each month. Just as the Moon pulls the ocean and creates the tides, it also pulls on the sea within our bodies, the blood. Moving with that cycle within us is another way that we have roots which connect us deep into the Earth and her movement. It also connects us with other women. Not only do we cycle with Grandmother Moon but when women gather together, we cycle together. Both the connection through our cycle to the Earth and to other women serve as roots which allow us to bend and dance with the wind rather than being uprooted."

"So that's why it is important to honor your Moontime and to take the time to be with other women."

"So you see, my little one, we are very much like these trees. We spread our branches and leaves reaching toward the sky with all that we do in our lives, nurturing others and accomplishing things but we must also create deep roots which give us support and sustenance from nature and our cycles. Being with other women helps to keep us balanced so we might weather the storms well and grow old in wisdom like this wonderful ancient tree. There is a song about the wind which to me means that wind and change can lead to wisdom and knowledge. Listen and then sing it with me to honor this tree:

Spirit of the Wind, carry me.
Spirit of the Wind, carry me home.
Spirit of the Wind, carry me home to myself."[1]

The Need to Honor Our Natural Cycle

As a therapist working with women over the last ten years, I have seen that many times the most common problems women experience, depression and anxiety, stem from a conflict between their own inner knowing and the environment in which they find themselves. Our fast-paced lives often involve playing many roles, from caretaker of children to bread winner, leaving us with little time to attend to ourselves and our own needs. Not only can we find many people and things outside ourselves to occupy our time, but our society teaches that this outward directed behavior is the ideal for women. At the same time we are encouraged to nurture others—children, our partner or spouse, our boss, other women—we are also encouraged to passively tolerate abuses and the anti-nurturing attitudes of our society and those around us. A conflict develops. How can we care for the children yet passively watch their abuse? How can we try to live a life of outward directed nurturing while we watch violence on our television, in the movies, on the street, and in our homes? Conflict produces stress. Lack of nurturing for ourselves produces stress. Nurturing others drains us unless we take time to replenish ourselves.

Another observation which I have made over the years is that men and women have very different natural cycles and these cycles are reflected in their structuring of time. Many, but certainly not all, men have a daily cycle which seems to include a period of work and a period of relaxation. In our society a typical work day for a man would be eight or nine hours. If they have a female partner, they use their time after work for watching television, socializing, reading, napping, etc. Women, on the other hand, particularly if they have children, work during the day either at child care or a paid job and also work at cooking, cleanup, and child care in the evening. It appears that women are much more likely than men to work throughout all their waking hours.

Consider this in the light of research done on hormonal changes in men and women. Studies show fluctuating testosterone levels for men throughout the day, with a peak in the morning and a low later in the day.[2] While one would not necessarily look at hormonal levels as having a primary effect on behavior, some evidence suggests that high testosterone (as well as high estrogen) levels are associated with better performance on automated tasks such as naming colors quickly, while low levels are associated with better performance on cognitive restructuring tasks such as finding embedded figures. Such fluctuations in ability in men have been found to occur on a daily basis, high automated task performance in the morning and high restructuring task performance in the afternoon.[3] Similar variations in task performance occur for women on a monthly cycle—high automated task performance at ovulation and high restructuring task performance at menstruation.[4] Being better at a restructuring task means that you are more creative, more open to possibilities, more open to change. Such research evidence confirms the observation that men and women, in general, operate on different cycles. This is not naturally a problem, only a difference. It becomes a problem, however, when women do not recognize their cycle or give validity to it, which is quite likely in a society based on men's cycles. Just as men would become highly stressed working all day and into the evening, women become highly stressed working at the same pace all month long. If one added up all the evenings that men rest and women don't, one would surely have enough time to be equivalent to four days worth of rest just before and during menstruation.

Unfortunately our society is patterned after a male model of cycling and male-oriented demands of productivity. This has not been true in all societies. Recognition of different cycles for men and women by most aboriginal people is seen in myths where the Moon is viewed as female (monthly cycle) and the sun is viewed as male (daily cycle). Anthropologists have given us accounts of many societies which were structured on the woman's cycle. For example, in the Yurok people of what is now California, the pattern followed the Moon and menstrual cycle. During the new Moon, women went together to the Moon lodge for renewal while the men went to the men's lodge or out to vision quest. At the full Moon, hunting and celebrations were held.[5] This, of course, would not preclude men from honoring their daily cycles within the larger cycle of women. In support of this, Margaret Henderson reported her research findings in a medical journal that when a man lives with a woman, his temperature cycle throughout the month synchronizes with hers, that is, a man shows a temperature rise and fall which approximates that of his wife.[6] If she becomes pregnant or is on birth control pills and, thus, does not ovulate, the man's pattern of temperature change stops as does hers. So even physically, then, there is a tendency for men to naturally follow a woman's cycle.

Most women I have spoken to about this say "Oh, how wonderful! Four days of rest and relaxation, I could handle that." The difficulty we find is how to put anything which is remotely honoring of our cycle into place in our daily lives.

While doing research on premenstrual syndrome (PMS), I observed that it was very difficult to get women with PMS together at the same time. They all were playing many roles at the same time. Either they were working more than one job in addition to raising children and keeping a home or they were balancing jobs with school, or some other combination which kept them busy every waking moment. Those who came to participate in a group were definitely highly stressed. It is interesting to note that a better predictor of PMS than "abnormal" hormone levels (which is not a good predictor at all) is whether a woman is married or not and whether she has children.[7] Those who are married with children have a much higher incidence of PMS than single women. It is also interesting that PMS symptoms increase with the existence of a male living partner.[8] While we are not saying that the husband is the cause of PMS (although I have seen a t-shirt which said "PMS—

Putting Up with Men's Shit"), the role of housewife and mother in our society is one which is conducive to stress.

Never before our present society has there been a culture which isolated women not only from their natural cycles but from each other. Child rearing and domestic activities are very solitary activities. There is evidence that the poorest psychological adjustment (more depression and anxiety) occurs in women who are married with children and do not have a paid job outside the home.[9] Both isolation and lack of value placed by society upon the work they do contributes to this effect.

Women in our culture play many roles and the old saying that a woman's work is never done is an understatement. Recent studies have indicated that, even when women's salaries are greater than their husband's salaries (which usually they are not), it is the women who still take primary responsibility for children and housework.[10] In their effort to be superwomen, women feel they must be the best mother, the best wife, and still do well at their job. The result is much stress and not much support for alone time. In fact, many women don't have the slightest idea what they would do with alone time if they had it. Women must take time alone regularly to feel comfortable with it. It is important for a woman to have that time to get to know herself apart from the roles she plays. She has a unique identity which is separate from being a mother or wife and separate from her work as well.

Just as the notion that women need alone time is not respected, there is not much support for women's growth and the two are related. In order for a woman to grow, she must have the time and space to reflect, to go into herself to look at who she is, what her lessons are, what her gifts are. Over thousands of years and all parts of the Earth, the traditional time for women to look inward has been during menstruation. But we are not likely to have husbands who say, "Just take the next four nights to yourself. I'll cook, take care of the kids and do housework." Nor are we likely to have friends who say "Let me take care of your kids during the day for the next four days so you can have time to yourself." Nor bosses who say each month "Take the next four days off from work, I know how important this alone time is to you." At least, I haven't heard of anyone saying those things. So how can women manage to find this alone time?

Women who do not have children or husbands probably spend more time alone and, thus, as research indicates, do not suffer as much from PMS. However single women can still stress themselves by staying too busy at the wrong time. Women who have children but are not currently married or living with someone often have a network of women friends who might support this time to themselves by taking care of the children for a period of time if they received the same favor in return. Women who live with or close to extended family or in a close knit community might also find free time more easily. Women who are married and have children must develop their husbands' appreciation for how important this alone time is to them so they can get their support, and they must develop a group of women friends who are willing to support them in their growth.

Since we no longer live in communities which honor this process, women must work to create the support for their growth process and alone time. In Japan, women are given menstrual leave.[11] Perhaps it is for the wrong reason, as many Japanese companies believe that women cannot work well at that time, but if women can use the time in a positive way for themselves, at least it is a beginning. I have heard of women in this country who use their sick days as "well" days and take one day off with each menstrual cycle. There are also women who cover for each other on the job to give a day or afternoon off at that time.

As women begin to see the value of taking this time, men and the society in general will also begin to value it. But at this point, it is not a matter of being given the time, it is a matter of taking the time.

What Happens When We Ignore Our Cycles?

So what exactly are the benefits of using our time of menstruation for inward work? We really need to look first at what happens when we do not use this time well. If women continue at their normal pace when their body is calling them inward, it leads to a variety of unpleasant effects. First, there is a great deal of irritability that develops because you are still running around meeting the needs of others when your need at that time is to honor your own body. Also, because you are most in touch at that time with your own truth, you find that what you see outside you often doesn't match your inner truth. If your truth tells you that people are supposed to live in harmony and act in a loving way toward each other, even listening to the news on television is a conflicting experience which can bring on both great anger and deep sorrow.

Just prior to and during our menstrual periods is a time of high sensitivity to the energy around us. If there is negativity around us, angry people for instance, we feel it very deeply. It is as if that energy comes inside us to live and it is often difficult to know whether there is something wrong with us or whether something out side us is causing the feeling. A woman might be much more affected than usual by even the violence on television.

With this extra sensitivity to the emotional energy around us, taking it all in like a sponge, we often are anxious, irritable, or depressed and don't know what to do with these feelings. So we may try to feel better by eating, usually the wrong things. Many of the foods we reach for to make us feel momentarily better, are the ones which make us feel much worse in the long run.

To make matters worse, we feel guilty that we are so emotional and sensitive and that guilt is reinforced by the tendency of men as well as other women around us to not take the things we are upset about seriously. I recall seeing a cartoon showing a husband sitting watching television and reading the paper while his wife is holding one screaming child and has two more clinging to her skirt. She is looking very frazzled, as though she might explode at any moment and she is holding a sign for her husband to read which says

31

"This is not PMS!" Many women have the experience of saying something very important about how something needs to change in their relationship only to be deflated by their partner's attributing their feelings to PMS, implying that they are temporarily insane, and ignoring them. This leads to both anger and depression.

Why Do We Ignore Our Cycles?

There are many reasons why we ignore our cycles. Certainly one of them is that women have fought so hard to try to get some level of equality in the work place that we don't want to give men any reason to discriminate against us. We are cautious here for good reason. Women pilots were barred from being captains on airlines because, some men said, "Would you want a woman with PMS flying the plane you were on?" For women who were directly competing with men in professional areas such as this, it was important to pretend that you didn't menstruate. Women have had a hard time deciding whether it is better to call PMS a defect of physiology or purely psychological. Both have implications for how they are viewed in competitive situations. In considering PMS on a larger scale, it is probably much more accurate to describe it as a spiritual defect of our society, particularly since there is evidence to suggest that it does not occur in many cultures.

So we ignore our cycles to prevent us from being discriminated against and ignoring our cycles leads to experiencing PMS which increases the discrimination against us—a vicious cycle.

We also ignore our cycle because of ignorance. Many of us were taught to view menstruation as something negative—"the curse"—something we would have to "put up with" for most of our adult years. With that kind of press, why would it ever occur to us that there could be anything positive about it or anything we should pay special attention to? About the only positive thing most women feel about its arrival is relief that least we were not pregnant. We also probably never really talk to anyone about our experiences of menstruation. Commercials tell us that we should not talk about menstruation and we must remove any evidence of it, visible signs or odor, or risk tremendous embarrassment. The taboo of silence in our culture prevents us from sharing our experience. Silence also keeps us from seeing any good models of how to experience menstruation positively. If there were any women out there who were honoring their cycles, taking alone time, finding their inner wisdom, who would know it?

We certainly have also been very much influenced by the attitude of our society that emotional ups and downs indicate psychological instability. So we try hard not to be "unstable" and, thanks to the medicalization of menstruation, if we are "unstable," we can attribute it to a physical cause, our hormones. Our choices are: pretend that our cycles are not cycles and be somewhat accepted by society—that is seen as "normal;" be psychologically unstable; or we can be physically defective. What wonderful choices!

What Does It Mean to Honor Your Cycle?

Let's look at another choice. The choice of honoring our cycle is not necessarily an easy one to make within a culture which is not cycle oriented. It is, however, a very powerful choice to make.

We have already pointed out the importance of taking alone time. There are several reasons that this is necessary. First, it allows us time for physical renewal. Rest, relaxation, play, freedom from responsibility, all nourish us, feeding our bodies so that we can be strong. I recall the guiding philosophy of a women's retreat camp in Montana: "A spiritual warrior knows herself to be the womb of creation and therefore has the love to take exquisite care of herself."[12] Women often put the care of their physical, emotional, and spiritual selves last after everyone else's needs are met. By doing that we can never be as strong and as powerful as we are truly capable of being. Alone time allows us to tune into our bodies to find out what they need. Rather than eating anything in sight just to feel better for the moment, we can find out what we can eat to truly nourish our bodies.

Alone time also gives us emotional renewal. We can get in touch with our feelings. Allowing ourselves to weep, we find what saddens us. Allowing ourselves to be angry, we find where our truth is not being honored. Allowing ourselves to acknowledge fear, we find where our challenges lie. We deal with our own emotions, letting them teach us rather than taking on everyone else's emotions and believing we are crazy.

Spiritual renewal comes from alone time. In solitary contemplation we find our connection to all things. We learn from the trees, the flowers, animals, birds and rocks. We see how we are connected to everything and experience oneness with the universe, with the Creator. We are at the same time one piece of the universe and the whole universe. We experience ourselves as the womb of creation. "The spiritual warrior knows herself to be the center of the universe and therefore has the courage to take exquisite care of herself."[13] From this alone time, this renewal, we are recharged physically, emotionally, and spiritually to move back into our daily activity with new energy and vision.

The hormonal shift which occurs at the time of menstruation moves us into a place where change can more easily occur. To reconstruct, to find new ways of seeing things, we must first let go of the old. Letting go leads to emptiness, sadness. But through emptiness we create the space for new things, new ways of being. Our cycle of hormonal change prepares us for this process each month. We can either fight it or take advantage of it. We may use it for growth by engaging in activities which allow the expression of our creativity. We shift to our right brain, the source of our creativity and playfulness. Dancing, singing, journaling, dreaming, drawing, painting, beading, sculpturing, gardening, or any other form of artistic expression will give voice to this process. None of it needs to make sense in a logical, rational, left brain way. It just needs to *be*.

Getting out in nature is also important when honoring your cycle. It is from nature that our cycles originate—the monthly cycle of the Moon pulling the tides within our wombs, the yearly cycle of renewal of the plants and trees. Our connections to these cycles in nature are affirmed when we spend time with these relatives. They teach us of the importance of cycles and help us to feel not only normal, but powerful and in sync with the movement of the Earth cycles within our bodies.

One of the things that we learn form older cultures about honoring Moontime is that our blood is sacred and needs to be respected. This is so contradictory to what our culture teaches that it is difficult to even think about it initially. Menstrual blood was the first blood on the altar, later to be replaced by animal sacrifices when patriarchy took over and this life giving blood was not available to men.[14] Native women went out to sit and bleed directly onto the Earth, to give back their blood as an offering to the Mother. Menstrual blood contains many nutrients and has been used by women over time for fertilizing crops and plants, despite unsubstantiated claims from a physician in the early 1900's that menstrual blood is toxic. Many of the women I know now who honor their blood, collect it and take great joy in using it to nourish the plants in their house and garden. Other women take care to dispose of the blood in an honorable way, such as burning the pads or tampons rather than sending them to the landfill. The Menstrual Wealth Catalog carries cotton pads which can be soaked in a Moon Bowl to obtain the blood for plants and the pads are then washed. Menstrual cups and sponges are available and make it easier to collect and use our blood in ways which acknowledge its sacredness. These items are reusable and further honor the Earth by preventing waste and lowering the demand for absorbent cellulose fibers (ground from tree wood).

To be able to honor your cycle, you must first know what your cycle is and tune into the changes that take place in your body and emotions over that cycle. Amazing things are learned when you keep track of your feelings, menstruation, and the Moon cycle. In Appendix A is a sample chart for keeping track of all of these together. Women who have done this have enjoyed the process as it helps you to learn about yourself.

Knowing where you are in your cycle is also helpful to allow you to take good care of your body. Our appetites change over the cycle and, when anticipated, these changes can be dealt with in a much healthier way by eating foods which satisfy cravings but are also good for you. Without this planning we often grab some junk food which accentuates the problem. There are also herb teas which help with some physical symptoms. Vitamins and minerals might also be lacking in your diet. Exercise is helpful in dealing with physical symptoms. We will talk about all of these in more detail in Chapter 7.

Another way of honoring our cycle is to use our feelings for learning about ourselves. This is discussed in detail in Chapter 6. Many women report feeling irritated just prior to their period. It is important to find out what it is that is irritating you, rather than thinking it is "just" PMS. It is probably something which irritates you all the time but you normally suppress your irritation in an effort to "make nice" or not make waves. Penelope Shuttle and Peter Redgrove describe this by suggesting that a woman's period may be, "a moment of truth which will not sustain lies." While a woman may be quiet about what bothers her during most of the month, "maybe at the paramenstrum, the truth flares into her consciousness: this is an intolerable habit, she is discriminated against as a woman, she is forced to underachieve if she wants love, this examination question set by male teachers in unintelligently phrased, I will not be a punching ball to my loved ones, this child must learn that I am not the supernatural never-failing source of maternal sympathy."[15] Emily Martin adds to this by saying that, "In order for women to see their rage as a blessing rather than a curse, it may be necessary for women to feel that their rage is legitimate."[16] Using our anger to teach us what needs to change in ourselves or in our lives is honoring our Moontime and the truth which it brings to us.

Spending some time going inward to find our inner teachers is also honoring. Using meditation in its various forms is important to help us hear our true inner voice, the voice of wisdom. Using dreams and art are also good ways to connect with this source of inner knowledge. Chapter 3 gives many possible ways you can begin this process. At the time when our brains are most prepared for inward journeys, we have the opportunity to find ourselves, to find the ancient truth within us.

In honoring our menstruation in these many ways, we begin the process of reclaiming our bodies, our power, and ourselves. It is a dance worth dancing at a time when many other dances in our lives have become meaningless if not painful. As we join together in this circular movement a healing takes place. There are many wounds to be healed. Women have been separated from each other and from their power. Healing means women joining together and supporting each other in assuming the power of the feminine. Men have been separated from their feminine sides. Healing means men who are more balanced in the use of their power to serve children and the generations to come. The connection between humans and nature has been broken. Healing means nurturing the Earth and understanding our relationship to all things in the Circle of Life. We have also been separated from our true selves as spiritual beings. Healing means knowing that we are magnificent beings with capabilities far beyond both our wildest imagination and our limited thinking, that we can restore peace, love and balance.

3

Relaxation, Meditation, and Inner Work

Circle

"With these stones I am marking the four directions and the boundaries of your Circle. The sun will be rising soon and you will stay in this small Circle until the sun sets. I will come for you then. Remember to pay attention to both your inner and outer worlds."

Dawn watched Grandmother disappear among the trees. "Well, this shouldn't be too hard," she thought. "I just need to stay in this Circle on this beautiful day until the sun sets. I can just see the red sun peeking through the trees now." As she looked around her, Dawn saw the first rays of the sun streaming through the leaves of the trees, shining on the dew drops in the grass. It made them sparkle and filled them with rainbows. The smell of the air was fresh with the fragrance of the flowers first blooming. As she listened, the stream nearby sang a song to the rocks over which it flowed.

She stood and faced the rising sun. "Welcome, Grandfather. Thank you for coming this morning to shine your light on my Circle. I'm here to learn more of what my gifts are and what my work is so

that I might better serve my people and the whole Circle of life."
She felt good that she had announced her intention to the sun and
sat back down.

"Now what?" she thought. "If I were home I would be busy with
chores, and I'd have lots of fun things to do." So she looked around
her again remembering Grandmother's words, "Pay attention."

A bird landed on a stone at the edge of the stream and took a
drink. She thought about what it must be like to fly like a bird and
stop wherever you want for a drink. But if she had wings to fly with
then she wouldn't have hands to make things with. "Hmmm" she
thought, "wouldn't it be nice to have both?" The bird left and
again she looked around her. The sun was still hanging in the sky
just above the horizon. Time did not seem to be passing very quickly.

"Well maybe if I just take a little nap, I'll be able to pay attention
better." So she leaned back against the tree which stood on the
edge of her Circle and closed her eyes.

When she opened her eyes she was left with an image of walking barefoot in the stream and splashing the cool water on her
arms and face. At that instant she heard a splashing noise and
looked up to see a doe and fawn standing in the stream. The fawn
was pawing the water with its foreleg while its mother drank. She
must have started when she saw the deer because the doe was
now staring directly at her and wagging her tail up and down.
Dawn remained motionless watching the deer. Then the doe blew
threw her nose making a loud snorting noise and Dawn jumped. In
an instant the doe and fawn were gone.

The sun was quickly dropping in the sky and Dawn stood tall in
the center of her Circle. She looked around her as she slowly turned
and faced each direction. She was filled with a sense of gratefulness to the teachers she met that day and she truly felt a part of all
that she saw. She heard Grandmother's voice singing through the
trees as the last rays of the sun touched her eyes. Their eyes met
but nothing needed to be said. She joined Grandmother's song as
they walked among the trees toward home.

The next morning Dawn went to find Grandmother. She couldn't wait to talk to her about all that she had learned the day before. Grandmother was sitting on a big rock near the pond.

"Oh Grandmother, I have so much to tell you!"

"Slow down now. Have you written your experience down in your journal yet?"

"Yes, I wrote last night until I fell asleep, and there was so much to say that my fingers still hurt."

"Some of what you learned is meant to share and some is meant just for you. You understand the meaning of some of it now and some will unfold and reveal itself to you later. Now, tell me a little of what you learned before you burst!"

"When I was writing about it I also found that some of it has no words. I felt something and I know what I felt—it was wonderful— but there were no words. Is that what you meant by understanding with the heart?"

"You have become so wise so quickly!"

"I guess the most important thing I learned which is also an understanding of the heart, and which I will try to put into words, is that I am connected to everything. I know I've heard you say that many times but now I really know it! And, because of that, everything is my teacher. Like the bird, who has the gift of flight, showed me how I have the gift of my hands. We both have different gifts and they are both beautiful. Then I saw that childhood should be a time to play just as the fawn played in the water, but motherhood is a time of responsibility. The doe was alert to the slightest movement to take her baby to safety. As I watched a butterfly drink the sweetness of the flower, I knew that we are all interdependent, the butterfly on the flower for food, the flower on the butterfly for pollination. It seemed as if the flower and the butterfly sang a song of beauty and love and they both were in perfect harmony! Do you want to hear their song?"

"I would like nothing better."

"Listen to our beauty song, Hey Ya, Hey Hey O Way.
We're calling you to sing along, Hey Ya, Hey Hey O
    Way.
Sing a song of Earth and Sky, Hey Ya, Hey Hey O Way.
Sing it loud and let it fly, Hey Ya, Hey Hey O Way.
When a Beauty Song is sung, We are One.
Hey Ya, Hey Hey O Way, Hey Ya, Hey Hey O Way."[1]

Relaxation and Meditation for Inner Knowing

If we look around the world we find that many cultures have a
more relaxed lifestyle than our own culture. The slower pace leads
to less stress and probably fewer stress related problems. Even
aboriginal people had rituals built into their society which provided
a time for relaxation and meditation.[2] A ritual of honoring the sun
at sunrise and sunset is a common one. Many world religions have
certain times of the day when prayers are said. Mexicans take a
siesta at mid-day. Research done in hospitals has shown that taking 15 minutes to meditate or consciously relax twice a day increases the ability of the immune system to fight off disease, it
decreases the reactivity of the body to stressful events and speeds
up recovery after major surgery.[3] Relaxation also decreases symptoms of PMS, even when symptoms are severe.[4] Other researchers have reported that, prior to their periods, women with PMS
symptoms have greater muscle tension which is an indicator of
stress.

Our culture is so masculine in nature, that is, so outwardly directed and goal oriented, that taking the time for relaxation and
inner-directed work often leads to guilty thoughts that you are not
doing something more "productive." Research seems to be in-
creasingly clear that relaxation is necessary for our good health as
well as a state of mental well-being. Children should be taught

early how to relax and meditate. Even sports psychologists use relaxation and visualization as primary tools for enhancing the performance of athletes. In working with people who are experiencing various kinds of psychological difficulties, I always teach relaxation. The inner work which follows often provides the healing solutions to the problems.

Learning Relaxation

So how do you learn to relax? There are many different methods which can be used to relax. There are whole books which describe various procedures, all of which are excellent. Over the years I have developed a reasonably short method of teaching relaxation which addresses both muscle relaxation and clearing the mind. I believe that both are necessary to be able to achieve and maintain a deep relaxed state. While many relaxation tapes exist, I don't suggest using them unless you are unable to achieve relaxation without them. People often become dependent on the tape and they may need to relax at a time when they either don't have or can't use a tape. Besides, it is very empowering to know that you, and you alone, have control over your body and mind. If you need to use a tape, make one of your own voice going through the various steps. That keeps the control within you. Playing soft music is fine, particularly in the beginning, if you want to achieve a very deep state of relaxation, or later for meditation. Learning deep muscle relaxation and how to clear your mind is the first step in learning to meditate and doing other kinds of inner work.

Ten Steps to Relaxation

1. Get in a comfortable position either lying down or sitting in a chair and close your eyes.
2. Begin by tensing your right arm, hold for 10 seconds and then relax; pay attention to the feeling of tension moving down your arm and out your finger tips; your arm should feel limp and heavy. Repeat.

3. Repeat Step 2 with your left arm.
4. Tense your face, wrinkling it up and clenching your teeth, then relax; let your teeth come a little apart and your jaw feel heavy, relax your forehead, eyebrows, eyelids, and cheeks; feel the tension draining away. Repeat.
5. Tense your shoulders for 10 seconds, pulling them up toward your ears while tensing across your chest and the back of your neck; then drop your shoulders letting them feel heavy and feel the tension come out of the back of your neck; take a deep breath and let it out slowly letting your chest feel more relaxed. Repeat.
6. Tense your stomach and abdomen as if you were doing a sit up, holding tight for 10 seconds; relax and let your stomach feel very comfortable. As you breathe in let your abdomen rise and as you breathe out let it fall and become more relaxed. Breathe in and out several times this way. Repeat.
7. Tense your right leg, pointing your toe up toward your knee and tensing all the muscles in your leg right up to your buttocks; hold for 10 seconds. And then relax; feel the tension flowing down your leg and out your toes; your leg should feel heavy and limp. Repeat.
8. Tense your left leg as in step 7. Repeat.
9. Think about your body parts, starting at the top of your head and working down to your toes, making sure all the muscles are relaxed, feeling heavy and limp. If you feel any tension try to let it go.
10. Picture a pleasant scene, such as a beach, a garden, a mountain lake, or a clearing in the woods, as vividly as you can, feeling the warm sun on your body. See this as a special place where you always feel good, peaceful, and very relaxed. Move your fingers, toes, and head in that order; stretch and open your eyes. You should now feel relaxed and refreshed!

Learning to relax takes practice. This whole procedure takes about 15 minutes and it should be done twice a day for one week. One good time to practice is at night when you go to bed—you can just go to sleep in the pleasant scene. Morning practice is also good because it sets a nice relaxed tone for your day. Another time which works well is when you are making a transition in your day, such as from work to home. Relaxing at that point helps to clear away the work thoughts and refresh you to continue on with your day. Generally, as you practice, you will achieve deeper states of relaxation and you will become aware of how you hold tension in your body.

When you choose a pleasant scene to use, it can be an imaginary place or a place you have actually visited, but you should always use the same scene. This scene is then linked in your mind with your body being in a very relaxed state. After awhile, just thinking of the scene will bring about instant relaxation. Many people find that they have difficulty concentrating on a scene. Their minds wander and get distracted with thoughts about all kinds of things. As soon as you become aware that you are distracted, re-focus on the scene or, if necessary, re-scan your body for tension and then re-focus on the scene. Do this as often as necessary, which might be 50 times or more in a few minutes. If you are very persistent in pulling your mind back to the scene, you will find that you are distracted less and less often. You must train your mind to focus concentration where you want it. This is also a good cure for worriers and excessive thinkers. Be as gentle and persistent with your mind as you would be with a young child. If you have always let your mind run off in all directions, do not be frustrated when you ask it to hold a pleasant scene and it can't. Being gentle and persistent will train it, teach it to work for and not against you. Discipline means teaching and you are teaching your mind to follow your commands.

After one week of practice you can begin with step 9, leaving out all the tensing and relaxing of the various muscle groups and just think down your body letting all the tension drain away. This can be achieved in about 30 seconds and you can then spend a longer time in your pleasant scene. At this point you can do the relaxation several times a day. You still need to be sitting or lying down with your eyes closed, but it takes a much shorter time and can be done in many situations. You may want to maintain 15 minutes or more of deeper relaxation each day for the general health benefits as well as stress prevention and the reduction of PMS symptoms.

By the third week of practice you should be able to completely relax your body and clear your mind in a few seconds, with your eyes open, while you are talking to someone. In the back of your mind you scan your body, releasing tension, and picture the scene. It is a wonderful tool for dealing with someone who is angry or likely to push your buttons. Maintaining yourself with both a calm exterior and interior allows you to reflect the emotion which is being directed toward you back to the source, allowing that person to own their own feelings.

Meditation

For many people raised in this culture, meditation seems like a mystery. We have learned to be very action-oriented and find "just" sitting still very unappealing, like wasting time. There are certainly many ways of meditating besides sitting still, although it is a very good place to start because it forces us to pay attention to what is going on inside us rather than allowing us to be distracted by activities or things outside. Once we understand how to hear our inner voice, we might find it easier to meditate while we do other things. Because controlling our thoughts is often an issue in meditation, it is easier to start with a guided meditation which keeps our attention focused than it is to simply sit down and let your mind empty out. Many people find they have to sit for at least a day before the constant chatter lets up and that can be very discouraging for the beginning meditator.

Perhaps another reason that we are not very familiar with the benefits of meditation is that we are also outwardly directed in our search for knowledge. In this culture we are told that we gain information from books, teachers, parents, priests, clergy, and other people who know more than we do. Little attention is given to the idea that we have access to all knowledge within us. If we quiet ourselves to hear the ancient voice, the true self, we have the solutions to all problems and the answers to all questions within us. Meditation is one way to hear that voice of knowledge.

I have included several guided meditations which seem to work well. There are also tapes and books which have meditations you can use, some of which are listed in Appendix B. Some people find that one particular meditation works well for them and others do not. Experiment and find one which works for you. An interesting meditation which can be a next step from your scene in the relaxation work is one which allows you to find an inner guide. When I refer to an inner guide, I think of this as a way of giving form to your inner knowing or inner wisdom. Some also think of this guide as your higher self or god-self. Others think of the guide as access to their unconscious, as a link to the universal consciousness (all knowing), or as a spirit guide. Think of it in any way that is comfortable for you. It is important to remember that however this guide (or guides) comes to you or however you understand the process, the information received can be trusted and will help you in your growth process.

Finding Your Inner Guide

Before beginning the meditation think of a question that you would like to have answered. Then relax your body and go either to your pleasant scene or to some other place where you know of a path which goes into some woods. Picture yourself walking along this path, paying attention to the scenery. Continue on the path, or go to a clearing and wait, until some person, animal, plant, or object draws your attention. This will be your guide. Ask the guide your question and wait for an answer. Sometimes long conversations occur, sometimes the guide will do something, and sometimes it appears that nothing happens. In this latter case, the answer to the question may come to you, seemingly out of the blue or in a dream, in the next few days. If it does not, repeat the question to the guide in another meditation.

Often new meditators feel that they are just making up what goes on in the meditation and don't trust the answers. After a little experience you will begin to trust the answers, seeing that they come from your own truth. You must believe in yourself and in the power of your own truth.

Many times I know I am not just making up the answer I learn because the answer is not what I want to hear, even though it feels right, deep within me. That, I believe, is a good test to use on information gained in any way—does it feel right deep within you, does it match your inner truth, your inner knowing.

Another meditation which I like to use with women is one which takes you to the Grandmothers. We can think of this Circle of ancient women as the ancient knowledge of women living within us or we can think of them as women in spirit guiding us now in our Earth walk. Think of them in any way that feels comfortable. You might want to tape this meditation with your own voice or have someone read it to you the first time you use it. After that you can go back very easily on your own. This is a wonderful meditation to do with the rhythm of the heart beat sounding on a drum.[5]

Going to the Grandmothers

Get yourself in a comfortable position sitting or laying down. Close your eyes and scan your body. Release all tension. Picture yourself standing on a beach. It is a nice warm, sunny day and the sand is warm on your bare feet. You are looking out over the water, watching the waves rolling up on the shore. When you look out, way out near the horizon, you see something in the water, maybe a boat. As you watch it come closer, you begin to see that it is a canoe, a large canoe. Soon it is coming up on the shore in front of you and you see two individuals paddling the canoe. These are your spirit guides for the journey. They invite you to step into the center of the canoe and indicate that they will take you to the Grandmothers. You step in and sit down, and they begin to paddle out over the water. Take a moment to look at these guides and see what they look like.

As the canoe moves smoothly over the water you look ahead and see some cliffs rising out of the water. At the base of the cliffs is a dark spot, and as you get closer, you can see that it is a cave or a tunnel. Soon the canoe enters the darkness of the tunnel. It is so dark you can see nothing. You hear the water dripping from the paddles. Soon you see a light which grows larger and brighter, and then you are out in daylight again. There is a shore-line, and as you approach you can see an animal waiting for you on the shore. Take a minute to study the animal.

The canoe pulls up on the shore and the guides indicate that you should go with the animal, it will lead you to the Grandmoth-ers and that they will wait for your return. You get out of the canoe and begin following the animal down the path. As you go, pay attention to the terrain here. What kind of plants and trees do you see? Soon you come to a place where you can see a large Circle of stones and sitting around this Circle is a group of women, old women. The animal says that it will wait for you and that you are to go to the Circle.

As you approach, one woman gets up and steps back so you may enter the Circle and then she sits back down. You stand in the center of the Circle and turn slowly to see all the women. One woman stands up and says that they are glad that you are here. They have been waiting a long time for you and are very happy to see you. They are here to guide you with their wisdom. They ask if you have any questions for them. You can ask a question if you like or you can just be with them for a while.

If you ask a question, pay attention to all that goes on. Some-times answers are not received in the form that you expect them and sometimes they come to you at a later time. After you have spent a little time with the Grandmothers, thank them for being there for you. They indicate that they are always there and you may come back anytime you wish, they will be waiting. One of them moves so you may walk out of the Circle and you walk back to where your animal is waiting. As you look back you can see them all smiling and waving.

The animal leads you back to the canoe and you thank the animal for guiding you. It indicates that it will be waiting for your return. You get in the canoe and enter the tunnel, the darkness. The light grows larger and you are again out on the open water headed back toward the beach where you began the journey. The canoe pulls up on the beach and you step out, thanking the guides. They respond that they will take you again, anytime you wish, that all you need to do is stand on the beach and look for them. You plant your feet in the warm sand and watch as the canoe disappears over the horizon.

Move your fingers, toes, and then head. Stretch and open your eyes.

This is always a good meditation to use when you have questions and are looking for inner guidance. You may vary the meeting with the Grandmothers, for instance, you may receive a gift from them. If you receive a gift, always take it from them in your left hand (left hand is the receiving hand, right hand the giving hand). Use the gift as a symbol of your lessons at that time. This meditation is also appropriate for men, although I usually change Grandmothers to Elders, which gives them the option of meeting with the Grandmothers or Grandfathers.

Inner Work

Inner work is much like meditation, except that it is more interactive with the various parts of yourself. We all have many aspects to our personalities, some of them which we are consciously aware of and some which are unconscious. The basic purpose of these exercises is to become more aware of ourselves in all that we are, to be more conscious of all that makes up who we are.

Being conscious of the physical body and its needs, our emotional process, the patterns in which our minds function and our spiritual connections is important for us to function as whole beings. In addition, we have within us the voice of the child, the male aspect, the female aspect, the ego, the wise one, and more. While we often hear conflicting voices in our heads, we usually do not take the time to identify which part of us is talking.

Eastern healing traditions speak of energy centers, or chakras, in our body which represent various aspects of our being. For a person to be well, the energy must flow freely among these centers. Dis-ease, then, is caused by blocks in energy flow through the chakras. Which chakra is blocked tells us about what kind of work we need to be doing to free up the energy flow. There are seven chakras, going from the base of the spine to the top of the head. The first, or base chakra, is in the area around the tip of the spine and pubic bone and is our connection to Earth or grounding chakra. The second is about an inch below the belly button and is the emotional chakra. The third is the solar plexus or just below the rib cage, and is the power chakra. The fourth, in the center of the chest at the level of the heart, is the heart chakra, concerned with unconditional love. The fifth is at the base of the neck, the throat chakra, and is how you speak out in the world. The sixth is referred to as the third eye and is just above the eyebrows in the center of the forehead. It represents your intuition and intellect. The seventh, the crown chakra, is right on the top of your head and is your connection to Spirit.

Steve Gallegos writes about a method of working with the chakras which involves finding an animal to associate with each chakra and then communicating with that animal about the functioning of that chakra.[6] This is an excellent way to give form to your inner process so that the process may become more conscious. The basic method used by Gallegos involves focusing on each chakra while in a relaxed state. You continue to focus until an animal appears or comes into your mind. When the animal comes, you observe it and ask it if it needs anything. What the animal is, how it behaves, and what it says is representative of what is going on for you in that chakra. After finding each animal and establishing communication with it, the animals are asked to come into a Circle and act your inner council. People who have done this exercise often find that they feel their animals' presence and hear their voices at various times when they need guidance. As you grow and develop the various parts of yourself, the animals may change. If you are interested in using this method, I recommend that you read Gallegos's book, *The Personal Totem Pole.*

It is also helpful to visualize a right and a left side animal. The right side animal is symbolic of your male aspect and the left side animal is symbolic of your female aspect. They provide a good way of working with the balance of female and male within you. Not only do both aspects need to be developed, but they must also work together for you to be centered and effective in the world. The female side carries with it the ability to go inside for information, the energy of emotion, the nurturing of all things, and the connection to the Earth. The male side carries with it the ability to manifest things in the physical world, rational and logical thinking, and the energy of the sun and sky. When these two aspects work together, the deep inner knowing of the female which comes out of the connection to the Earth and nurturing of life is manifest into the physical world through the skill of the masculine aspect. Women in our culture often have both male and female aspects developed, since the masculine is necessary for success in the educational system and the workplace, but they don't always work well together. There is, instead, often conflict between intuition, or inner knowing, and what the masculine says needs to be done. Developing a dialog between the left side and right side animals is symbolic of communication between the male and female aspects. The same process can be done effectively by imagining your inner male and female as people rather than animals. Animals are often the guides for traditional shamanic healing journeys, but you may use any imagery which is comfortable and effective for you.

It is popular now to do work with one's inner child and there are many books and workshops which address the issue of re-parenting the inner child to deal with the effects of growing up in a dysfunctional family. The child is one voice of the many that make up your inner dialog. It is important to listen and be able to pick out the child's voice, for it is often the voice of fear, insecurity, negative self-statements, anger, stubbornness, and feelings of helplessness. When we were children, we all experienced situations where we could not defend ourselves, or where our knowledge of the truth of a situation was denied by adults around us. These situations made us feel helpless and deny trust in ourselves. Now as adults who have the ability to take care of ourselves and who can speak our truth, we still hear the child's voice telling us we can't. If we can recognize when this inner child is speaking, we can put that voice into perspective and by understanding the source of the information overcome the doubt.

Another way of working with this inner child is to image the child while in meditation. You might look at pictures of yourself as a child and find one which stands out and use that image. In the meditation you can then talk to the child in a very loving way, telling her that you will take care of and protect her. Help her to feel important and thank her for doing what she needed to do back then to help you survive. Then tell her that she doesn't need to be angry or frightened or use her usual way of coping because you now have the ability to do what needs to be done for both of you and that she can trust you to take care of her. This type of positive affirmation of the child might be repeated anytime you hear her frightened, angry, or self-depreciating voice in your inner dialog.

The ego is another voice often heard in inner conversations. I think of the ego as the aspect of ourselves concerned with our image as seen by others or by the society. It is concerned with doing the right thing, being the good girl, being successful, not being selfish, being liked by others, being seen as a good wife and mother, and following the "rules." It is the voice of our social-ization process speaking within us that tells us how we "should" be and we can often recognize it because it uses the word "should" a lot. This is a voice which needs to be questioned and compared with the voice of your inner truth or Wise One. While it is impor-tant to fit in to a community and follow rules set up for the good of all, this doesn't mean that you cannot also follow your own inner truth. In a system which truly works for the good of all, there will not be a conflict. By questioning the ego voice, we find the places where our society needs to be changed.

While reading a book by Becca Zinn, I found the name of a familiar voice in my inner dialog, the voice of doubt.[7] This is the voice you hear when you are on the edge of a cliff, about to use the newly formed wings which you have worked so hard to grow. You are ready to soar with the eagles into freedom when the voice of doubt says, "Yeah, but what if they don't work, what if you fall?" This voice is always there to give energy to your doubts, undermine your trust in yourself and in the universe. Recognize this voice and very nicely tell it to shut up.

The voice of the Wise One is the voice we must strain to hear above the clamor. She is our inner truth, the One Who Knows. We often hear but ignore Her voice because what She tells us to do is not what we think we want to do, or because what She tells us to do is too hard, or because we fear we might meet with resistance from those around us if we follow Her counsel. Following this voice takes a great deal of courage and trust.

There are many other voices we hear as well, because we are very complex beings. There is the voice of our body which tells us about our physical needs, what we need to be eating, what will heal us, how much rest we need. Of course we also have the mother and father figures within us. They play an important role in nurturing the inner child and letting her know how much she is loved and how wonderful she is in a way that most children did not experience it from their parents.

Jungian analyst Clarissa Pinkola Estes has written about the Wild Woman archetype.[8] An archetype is a universal form which exists in all of us. In her book, *Women Who Run With The Wolves*, she describes the Wild Woman as the part of us which is in touch with our basic instincts, creativity, and freedom. We hear the voice of the Wild Woman calling us to play, run barefoot in the meadows, and bathe in the cool streams. She is a particularly important and empowering voice now as we move away from being the well-controlled, proper, make-everybody-happy ladies which our society idealizes. As we reclaim the feminine, we must also reclaim the Wild Woman within us.

In working with these inner voices, the goal is to bring them into a council where they can work in harmony for the common good and your growth. To develop the communication necessary for this to happen, you must identify the voices and assess their needs. For example, the child might be feeling unworthy and helpless. In response to these feelings she gives you messages which make you feel worthless and depressed. You need to listen to this child talk, perhaps from the role of the inner mother, and tell her what she needs to hear. A Gestalt therapy technique which works well here is to sit facing an empty chair. Imagine that your inner mother is sitting in the chair. You are the child talking to her and telling her how you feel and what you need. It is important to do this out loud even though you might feel a little foolish. When the child is finished, switch chairs and become the mother who will reassure the child and tell her how important she is. The mother should tell the child that her feelings will not be ignored and that she can trust her mother to be there and protect her. Sometimes it is helpful to have a friend there to witness this exchange and prompt the mother to say nurturing things.

Similar exchange can be worked on between male and female aspects, getting them to talk to each other and work together rather than opposing each other. In its early stages, doing this work is a little like doing family therapy internally. The conflicting voices need to work together, each of them providing important information for your growth.

Nature as Teacher

Once we open up to our inner world, everything around us becomes our teacher. We have already talked about using animals as inner teachers but they can also serve as symbols in our daily encounters with them. Each animal has its own specific lesson to teach us. We might discover these lessons by watching the animals or we can use tools such as the Medicine Cards.[9] These are a set of cards each with an animal on it and a book which talks about the lessons, or medicine, of each animal. They function like a tarot divination. Plants are also good teachers. They teach us of cycles, about having roots in the Earth for nourishment and flowering in beauty.

Symbols are important to give us a way to interpret our experience. An ancient symbol system is the medicine wheel, or Circle of stones. Circles of stones have been found all over the world, constructed by our ancestors to represent their understanding of the universe within and without. Almost always there are spokes on the wheel which point to the four directions. While there are many slightly different symbolic qualities which are attributed to the directions, the one which I will share is somewhat of a composite of several wheels used by North American Indians.

The East is the place of vision and newness, yellow, masculine, manifesting, springtime, new shoots, dawn, infancy, the great eagle who sees far. The South is the place of trust and innocence, red, summertime, physical world, midday, child and young adulthood, flowering, mouse, turtle, or coyote. The West is the place of introspection, going within, black, autumn, sunset, feminine, old age, fruit, the great bear who hibernates. North is the place of wisdom, the ancestors, spiritual world, death and rebirth, white, night time, winter, quietness, seeds, the buffalo or snowy owl.

Each direction represents a part of ourselves. As we move throughout our lives we travel around the wheel, working on the issues symbolized by each direction. At the same time, with each trip around the wheel we move closer to the center and upward in a spiral. Often we experience an issue, trust for instance, and think we are done with it, only to have it come back again as we continue our circling around the wheel. If lessons have been learned the first time, even though the issue seems very familiar, the second and third time around we are working on a much deeper level and we are much closer to being in our center. The symbol of the Medicine Wheel has been very helpful to me in interpreting information gained in meditation, dreams, nature, and everyday life. There are many good sources of information on the wheel if this particular symbol system appeals to you.[10] However, any symbol system will work if you use it consistently.

Another way of using nature as a teacher is to take time to be by yourself outdoors. Native Americans engaged in vision quests by being alone outside for four days and nights without food or water. This type of ritual, however, is found in many variations all over the world. I have been involved with a women's vision quest camp with Brooke Medicine Eagle for several years, doing both my own questing and assisting other women with their first quests. I am consistently amazed at the transformation which occurs within me and in others from staying within a small Circle out in nature for two days and nights. Everything, both inside and outside, becomes your teacher, and because you are not busying yourself with many other things, the lessons are learned on a very deep level. While not everyone can travel to a vision quest camp, there are ways in which you can seek the teachers in nature on your own. A good start is to go to a park for a day, or even an afternoon, to sit in a Circle which you have marked with stones in the four directions. While you are there, listen to the inner voices and pay attention to what is going on around you. (Try not to take food, as it is distracting, although water is fine.) This is also a wonderful thing to do with a friend. You would, of course, be sitting far enough apart so that you could not see or hear each other, but you would then have someone with whom to share your experiences and who will have some understanding of their significance.

Regardless of where you begin your journey within, just prior to and during your Moontime is when you are most open to change and seeing things in a new way. Using this time well means honoring the cycle of change which is naturally occurring within you by taking the time to listen.

4

Dreams and Journals

Dream time

"How are you doing with the dream journal?" Grandmother asked as she brushed and braided Dawn's hair.

"It is to hard to remember the dreams long enough to write them down. And then when I do, most of my dreams seem too silly to bother with."

"Dreams are the deep parts of ourselves communicating with us. They tell us what our lessons are and what we need to attend to. In a way they are an inner teacher just as the animals, plants, rocks, and other people are outer teachers."

"But they don't make much sense most of the time."

"Understanding the message of a dream is like a puzzle. Each part must be understood as it fits into the whole. Do you remember how we said that a tree can be a symbol that teaches us how to live? Well, our dream images are symbols too. It is not the actual image in the dream that is important, it is what it represents to us."

"OK, let's see if you can make sense out of this one. Last night I dreamed that I was in school and the teacher asked me a question. I knew the answer but when I opened my mouth a bird flew out and landed on her head. The whole class jumped up and tried to catch it. And then I woke up."

"How did you feel in the dream?"

"I felt good and maybe a little surprised while I was dreaming, but when I woke up and thought about it, I felt embarrassed."

"Let's think about what that bird represents to you."

"Well, I always think of birds as having the freedom of flight. They can go where they want to and have no restrictions."

"Is there any way in which you have been feeling restricted, especially in how you express yourself verbally?"

"Well...there is a group of friends that I've been feeling frustrated about. There are times when they do things or say things I don't agree with, but I don't say anything to them about it because I don't think they would like me very well if I did."

"How did the other students in your dream feel when the bird flew out of your mouth?"

"Oh they wanted the bird. They each were trying to catch it for themselves!"

"And the teacher, how did she react?"

"That was really odd. She just stood there and smiled with this bird sitting on her head."

"So if we relate the dream to the situation with your friends, what do you think your inner teacher is trying to tell you?"

"I guess the bird might have represented the freedom to say what I really feel rather than the answer I knew they expected. So when I spoke my true feelings, when the bird flew from my mouth, the teacher, who is probably my inner self was happy. And the other kids really wanted to hear what I said and maybe they wished they could say what they felt too?"

"This seems like the correct interpretation to you. So how will you use this dream?"

"I guess it means that I don't need to be afraid to say what I really feel and that I must speak my truth to be happy with myself. Wow, and I thought it was just a silly dream."

"Often it takes some work to put the pieces of the puzzle together. That's why it is important to write dreams down so you can work on them. It's especially important to pay attention to your dreams just before and during your Moontime. That is often when the messages are the clearest and the most important."

"Thank you so much, Grandmother, for this lesson. I'm going to get my dream journal and try to put some more puzzles together."

"We will talk more of dreaming again but, for now, you have enough knowledge to start learning the wisdom of your inner teacher in your dream school. Owl also teaches us of dreaming since she is the keeper of the night. A song about Owl, who is called Pueo in Hawaiian, goes like this:

Pueo, Pueo, sweet keeper of the dream
Your wings open above me
You teach me how to sing my deepest song
In darkness I find you, Goddess of the night
You tell me turn inward
There you'll find the light for your journey.
The journey is endless, a dance of shadow and light
I call upon my vision
I offer you my sights and my wisdom
Pueo, Pueo, you teach me how to sing my deepest
    song
Your wings open within me
Sweet keeper of the sacred song."[1]

The Importance of Dreams

Dreams have been seen as significant by many cultures, both ancient and modern. They have been used within many different psychological theories in a variety of ways, all giving significance to the dream as a reflection of inner workings of the person. Dreams have been used in similar ways since the beginning of time. Native Americans often viewed dreams and visions as communication from the spirit world. Seneca Indians felt that dreams should be acted out to prevent misfortune. Dreams were also seen to have special significance at the time of menarche, or the first menstrual cycle. Hilary Maddux reported that among the Shasta Indians, a girl was secluded with her mother in a menstrual hut for ten days at menarche. At night she was kept awake and only allowed a brief sleep just before dawn. She then told her dream to her mother. The dreams were a guide for the girls life.[2] We know from scientific studies that sleep deprivation increases dreaming. This ritual, therefore, insured that the girl would dream intensely. There are also reports in the literature that girls are likely to dream about menstruating before menarche. Dena Taylor recalled that both of her daughters dreamed that they were menstruating the night before their first period came.[3] This suggests that in some way, our dreams carry body knowledge of which we might not be consciously aware.

In addition to the importance of dreams around menarche, several researchers have tracked women's dreams throughout the menstrual cycle, finding that dreams are more vivid and active just prior to menstruation and more passive and receptive during ovulation. Penelope Shuttle and Peter Redgrove report research done in the 1940s in which it was found that heterosexual dreams preceded ovulation while relaxed contented dreams occurred during ovulation.[4] Receptive dreams involving pregnancy or babies occurred right after ovulation and then more energetic and active dreams prior to menstruation. Other common dream images included eggs, jewels, and round fragile things at ovulation and broken egg shells, sex, talking animals, and violence at the time of menstruation. A rise in sexuality and anger in dreams and dreams of change occurred more often premenstrually.

Another premenstrual dream image which has been reported frequently is the appearance of an inner man, or sometimes inner woman, as a comforter. This inner man has been characterized as the Moon lover by a number of different cultures. A strange man in the dreams is more likely at this time either in the role of lover or companion. Marilyn Nagy suggests that this strange man is like an other-worldly lover which appears in menstrual mythology and that he represents opposition to the present state of things. "The attributes of the image, together with the affective qualities attached to it may indicate the direction along which a change in consciousness is taking place."[5] She says, "Every lover comes first as an unknown stranger and promises a woman both great joy and great danger."[6] This strange inner lover, thus, beckons the woman to personal psychological development. According to Robert Van De Castle, women take more active social roles toward males in their menstrual dreams.[7] Evelyn Reynolds demonstrated how menstruation dreams may assist women's personal integration.[8]

In his books on dreaming Ernest Hartmann reports that women dream more often, more vividly, and with more sexual content just before and during menstruation (days 25-30 of our cycle).[9] He also found that premenstrual symptoms are worse when women do not get enough sleep and improve if they sleep more than usual, suggesting the importance of dreaming at this time. Brooke Medicine Eagle talks about the importance of menstrual dreams from a Native American viewpoint:

> The information received as the menses begins is the clearest human picture from within the womb of the Great Mystery, of the unknown and our future. Among our dreaming peoples, the most prophetic dreams and visions (of the coming of the white peoples

and other such almost incomprehensible changes) were brought to the people through the Moon Lodge.[10]

Native people have also viewed dreams as a way of moving within the spirit world. This other world which exists concurrent with the physical world is referred to as the Dreamtime. In this realm much work can be done, healing work, communication with others in another place, finding the answers to problems. In Mary Dillon's fictional book on first menstruation for a young native girl, Kory dreams during her first Moontime of going to a distant village and healing a cataract in an old woman. Several weeks later, news comes to her village about this woman's healing along with a gift for Kory.[11] There are a number of recent books which address the dreaming women of some of the Mexican Indian tribes, giving personal accounts of this type of dreaming process.

In 1988 Dena Taylor gave a questionnaire to a large number of women. One question was "Are your dreams different around the time you are menstruating?" Following are some of the answers:

They feel prophetic and important. I pay attention to them. They seem more meaningful

More visionary/lucid/regressive/receptive.

Unravels my soul.

Usually more intense and sexual.

More people oriented.

More emotional, lots of people from different parts of my life, lots going on.

I realized today during my last bloods I had a very impressionable dream with a message I had been seeking.

I tend to experience deep emotional intensity in my dreams. They are also more vivid and easier to recollect. I feel more connected to the underworld, my subconscious.[12]

Many women I have talked to about dreams report similar experiences, with the majority finding that the dreams just prior to and during menstruation are more vivid and meaningful. While dreams can be useful sources of inner information at anytime, dreams around the time of our Moon, when we are naturally in touch with the inner sources of wisdom, can be especially informative.

Dream Work

While meditation and inner work can be done on a conscious level, dream work provides another method for communication with the various aspects of yourself. There has been much written on the interpretation of dreams and the meaning of specific symbols. While some symbols may be fairly universal, it is probably more accurate to view the dream within your personal symbol system. If your inner self wishes to communicate with you, it will use a language familiar to you, using the meanings which you personally assign to various symbols.

Probably the most difficult part of interpreting dreams (other than remembering them!) is getting past the literal aspect of what happened in the dream to see the symbolic meaning. For example, a person may dream of dying, then wake up, think about it, and become frightened, even when there was no feeling of fear in the dream. Upon waking, the fear occurs in response to the literal interpretation—that you are dying. The symbolic interpretation may be that there is a change taking place within you. Change is often symbolized by death. You are letting go of parts of you which are no longer needed and making room for new things to develop. While there are certainly many types of dreams and different ways of interpreting the same dream, you should always trust the voice of your inner Wise One as to the validity of the interpretation. If the interpretation *feels* right to you, then it is right. One useful way of interpreting a dream is to look at all of the characters in the dream as aspects of yourself. For example, you as well as all the other people in the dream may be playing the roles of your inner female,

male, child, ego, etc. An animal may also represent an aspect of you. An activity may be symbolic of some quality you have.

A Jungian view of dreams is that they allow us access to our shadow selves. The Shadow is a part of ourselves which we do not accept or which we have not yet realized. For example, when we dislike a quality in another person, we are projecting that quality from our Shadow and do not see it as part of ourselves. This also works with positive qualities which we admire in others but have not yet made real in ourselves. The Jungians say that the unconscious part of ourselves, our Shadow, reveals itself to us in our dreams. Perhaps our cultural upbringing has suppressed our instinctual nature, the free and intuitive aspects of ourselves as women. We might then dream of a wounded animal or a locked door in the basement, representing our wounded instinctual self or the part of ourselves we locked away early in our lives. As we become aware of these aspects of ourselves we can begin the process of integrating them into our conscious selves, and, thus, become more of who we really are. Dreams, then, serve the function of bringing Shadow to consciousness.

There are some excellent books on Jungian approaches to women's dreams. Marion Woodman traces the course of three women's journeys through dream analysis as they bring their deep feminine to consciousness and leave patriarchal consciousness behind.[13] Clarissa Pinkola Estes addresses the Wild Woman archetype, tracing the growing awareness of the feminine instinctual self through dreams and fairy tales.[14] Both books are excellent for anyone seeking to know more about the Jungian approach from a feminine viewpoint.

There are also excellent tapes on dreaming and the wild woman archetype available through Sounds True Catalog. In Estes's tape on dreams, *In the House of the Riddle Mother,* she talks about dreams having three parts, the setting, the conflict, and the resolution.[15] I have found that using this structure is helpful in making sense out of many dreams. For example, in Dawn's dream the setting would be the school room. The conflict was the unexpected bird coming from her mouth rather than the answer. The resolution was the bird landing on the teacher's head and the whole class trying to catch it. When seen in this format, the interpretation becomes clear more easily. Estes also talks about common images in women's dreams such as animals, frightening men, toilets, etc., and their possible meanings. Woodman, in her tape called *Dreams: Language of the Soul*, discusses the Black Madonna archetype in women's dreams as representing the suppressed side of the feminine.[16] Woodman says that this image is coming to women and men more and more in their dreams as we grow closer to bringing the feminine into consciousness. Both of these tapes are very helpful aids to begin the process of interpreting your dreams to enhance your growth process.

Remembering dreams, of course, is the first step to using dreams as a tool for growth. Many people say that they do not dream, while science tells us, from recording brain activity, that everyone dreams several times each night. As we sleep, we change in levels of consciousness from a light sleep, to a deep sleep, to dreaming, and back to a light sleep again repeating the cycle several times. The time we are most likely to wake up is in a transition from a dreaming state to a light sleep and it is at that point that we are left with the lingering images of the dream. If we move, those images fade very quickly. One way to improve your dream memory is to replay the dream in your head when you wake, before you move at all. Then once you have replayed it like a movie, write it down or speak it into a tape recorder as soon as possible. The more details you have, the easier it is to interpret later. You should also record how you were feeling in the dream. Don't worry about interpreting it while you are replaying it and don't think that the dream is just silly, junk or too bizarre to record. Even little pieces of dreams can have important information.

It takes a lot of discipline to be consistent with writing down dreams. It might be a good beginning to write down one dream which occurs just before or during each Moontime. You can then use that dream in your meditation. There are several ways to work with a dream in meditation. One way is to relax and then run through the images of the dream again, allowing your mind to make any digressions or changes it wishes. Another way to work with the dream is to take it to your meditation guides and ask for help interpreting it. For example, if you have developed a relationship with the Council of Grandmothers you can go and tell them the dream and ask them what it means. Or, your chakra animals can be asked to come into a council and you can present them with the dream. You could also gather together your inner aspects, male, female, child, ego, Wise One, etc. and ask them to give you feedback on the dream. You may also have developed other inner guides who can clarify the significance of the dream. An interesting way to get further clarification on a dream is to ask for another dream before you go to bed the next night. If you remember your dream, you can see how the two dreams relate to each other.

A lucid dream is a very interesting and useful phenomena. In a lucid dream you know that you are dreaming and consciously direct the course of the dream. It is a way of being consciously aware while you are dreaming and doing inner work while you are asleep. If you wake up aware that you have been dreaming, remain relaxed and don't move. Replay the dream a little so that you can get back into it. It may feel like you are half awake and half asleep. You may be able to fall more deeply asleep and change or finish the dream any way you want to.

I recall waking and remembering a dream in which two friends had told me to take their airplane out for a spin. I got in and began to taxi out to the runway, all the time thinking about how I didn't know how to fly a plane and that I didn't want to mess up their airplane. By the time I got to the runway, I had talked myself out of flying it and taxied it back and told them that I couldn't fly it. At that point I woke up, became aware of the dream, and said to myself, "You chicken, get back there and fly that airplane, it's only a dream!" I went back into the dream, got in the airplane, taxied out to the runway and took off. I woke up again feeling great. Learning to take an active role in your dreams is a way of making the unconscious conscious.

Another way of directing your dreams, is to go to bed consciously asking for a dream as an answer to a problem. Our dreams tap into the deep creativity within us and can often provide us with the material for very creative solutions which we otherwise might consciously block. Working in meditation with whatever dream comes will facilitate this process. Even if you do not remember a dream that night, when you wake think again about the problem, since the time right after waking is also a good time for creative insights to break through.

Collective dreams are also interesting to explore. Patricia Garfield indicates that couples who sleep in the same bed soon synchronize their brain wave patterns and, thus, their dream time is also synchronized.[17] There is also some suggestion that they may dream of similar topics but with different symbols. Another similar finding is that babies who sleep with their mothers, synchronize their brain waves and wake-sleep cycles with the mothers.

It is possible that women who are connected through their synchronous Moontime might also dream similarly. If you have a group of women with whom you are working on personal growth, it is sometimes fun to share Moontime dreams or keep them in a group dream journal. As we are connected to each other as bleeding women and on a spiritual level, so also are our dreams connected. This is evidenced in the commonalties in women's dreams across the cycle. If each of us can dream a piece of the puzzle, and when we put our pieces together, we all have a better sense of what the whole picture is.

The Journal

There are many types of journals which can be kept. How you use a journal may change depending on what you are working on at a particular time in your life. There are dream journals, meditation journals, feelings journals, dialog journals, etc. I believe that we make the most of our lessons in life when we keep some kind of journal or record. This of course takes time and it is best to start with something you can easily do rather than have grandiose plans and fail. It probably makes most sense to begin with journaling around your Moontime. Initially the journal could take the form of daily ratings with occasional comments on the ratings (a form you can use for this type of journaling appears in Appendix A). It will help to increase your awareness of your cycle of emotions and physical changes in relation to what is happening in your life and the Moon. You could also begin with a dream journal in which you record your dreams on one page and write about the dream—your interpretation of it and any meditation on it—on the next page. This also allows you to enter any other pertinent information about what is happening in your life. Another possibility is a meditation journal. This would be a record of your experience during meditation which would be written following your meditation exercises. Feelings and dreams related to the meditation could also be included. Certainly you can create one large journal in which you would write daily, recording dreams, meditations, thoughts, feelings, what's going on externally and internally and anything else you wish to enter. For this type of journal it is good to set aside a particular time each day to write in it. While dreams should be written down as soon as possible whenever they occur, a good time to write in this more general journal is before bedtime. It allows you to integrate your day and may stimulate your dreaming.

Journals can also be used for very specific growth work. The different inner aspects of yourself can each be given a voice in a journal. Every journal is a dialog with yourself and identifying the voices of your different inner aspects through journal writing can be illuminating. For example, if you are experiencing an inner conflict, write down each view of the conflict and try to identify which aspect of yourself is expressing that view. This awareness can give you a better understanding of how the conflict can be resolved. Writing can also be a good way to clarify your feelings about something. Having to put the issues and feelings into words gives us greater understanding of what actions we might want or need to take.

Women often find that they have difficulty in finding their voice when it comes time to speak their inner truth. Some of this comes from the fear that what they say will not be well-received or that they will not be able to say it so that others will understand. Writing what you wish to say in the form of a letter to whoever you wish to speak with is a good way to go about this process. It not only gives you the opportunity to get everything said the way you want to say it with no interruptions, but seeing it on paper also makes it more real and increases your courage to find your voice. You may want to give the person the letter and then discuss it, or you might find that the act of writing it enables you to say what you want to say.

Whatever form you decide upon, journaling is an excellent tool to facilitate your growth process. It provides a record of your growth so you can see your progress. Without such a record it is easy to begin feeling like you have made no progress at all, particularly in the most trying times when you are struggling with the most important issues. Being able to look back through your journal and see the growth and deepening of your spirit, provides the strength to go on into the darkness.

5

Bellies and Shields

The Drum

It was growing dark. Dawn sat on a pillow by the fireplace watching the flames dance along the log. Grandmother came in, lit a candle and the delicious smell of sage and sweetgrass smoke wafted through the air. The rocking chair squeaked as Grandmother sat down. She picked up her drum and began to play softly. Dawn closed her eyes as the familiar sound of the drum vibrated her eardrums, her body, bringing her own heart in time with its slow heartbeat rhythm.

"Do you feel the vibration of the drum in your belly, Dawn?"

"Oh, yes. It seems like it vibrates my whole body!"

"Just as your belly receives the rhythm of the drum, it also receives other vibrations that are around you. In a way, your belly is like a drum. It needs to be tuned, not too tight and not too loose, so that you can receive the vibrations of others. We all create vibrations of energy around us. You know how we talk about a person having good or bad vibes? We sense that through our belly drums."

"I know what you mean. It's like walking into a room where people are mad at each other. The air feels thick with tension. So I'm picking up that vibration in my belly?"

"That's right. Sometimes when we are around a negative energy situation like that we end up with a belly ache, although most people are not aware that it comes from outside themselves rather than inside. It is helpful to develop an awareness in your belly so that you can focus your attention there. The first signals of walking into a dangerous situation are felt in your belly. The belly is actually the center of your body and walking with the body erect, head up and belly leading will help to bring your attention to the belly and you will be moving from your center. You are then prepared for anything, and moving in a balanced way."

"I remember that you showed me that when I was younger. I try to walk that way especially when I am alone. It makes me feel stronger and more powerful."

"It's good that you have already practiced. One of the things you need to learn now is how to protect yourself from negative or unwanted energy. This is especially important now that you will be cycling with the Moon. Just before and during your Moontime your belly is extra sensitive to vibration. This is good because it allows you to receive energy and wisdom from spirit and nature around you. It can also be a problem if the energy of the people around you is negative, because you will absorb it like a sponge. Grandmother Moon teaches us to withdraw from our everyday lives and move more into ourselves at that time. It is important to have more alone time and to be careful about what situations you put yourself into. That would not be the best time to confront an angry person or to be around large numbers of people. But since we cannot always avoid those situations, another way of protecting yourself is to have a shield for your belly."

"Do you mean I should actually make a shield and wear it over my belly?"

"You may want to physically construct a shield to remind you to use your belly shield, but it isn't necessary to do that. The shield I'm referring to is one that you imagine. There are many ways to

74

imagine a shield to protect you from unwanted energy. Some people think of a light surrounding them through which only positive energy can pass. My favorite is a shield which has a mirror on the outside. If someone directs negative energy toward me it simply reflects back to them."

"But how does it work? Do you have to be thinking about it all the time?"

"You have to consciously visualize putting your shield in place before you enter a situation, but after that it is really only takes minimal awareness."

"What happens it you forget to put the shield up and some negative energy comes your way?"

"Then you must consciously cycle the negative energy out of your body. This can be done through breathing. Think of every exhalation as releasing the energy down through your feet into the ground to let the Earth recycle it. Or you could exhale and move the negative energy from your belly up to your heart and out of your body, with love, back to the source—as long as the energy moves through and out of your body."

"What happens if it stays?"

"Then you will experience a negative emotion such as anger or fear or depression and it won't be your emotion. Your might even begin to think it is yours and feel that something is wrong with you. One way to tell whether an emotion comes from you or from outside you is to listen to how you describe it. If you say 'I feel angry' then it is not yours. If you say 'I am angry' that comes from you. Many of our emotions are picked up from others around us and sometimes even from events that are happening in another place or perhaps happened in the place where you are but long ago. As we become more aware of this process, it becomes much easier to sort it all out. So you need to do some work on finding the right shield for you and practice using it."

"I'd also like to actually make a shield and hang it in a special place to remind me of this teaching. Will you help me with that, Grandmother?"

"As soon as you can visualize your shield, I'll get you started on making it. There is a song that speaks of our hearts as drums, also, beating in synchrony with other's hearts. Listen while I sing it for you along with the heart beat of this drum:

"She stretched my heart, made it a drum keeping time
    with everyone
She stretched my heart, made it a drum keeping time
    for dancing
with the Moon and stars and sun, keeping time with
    everything
keeping time for dancing with the rain and the wind, in
    a Circle of friends."[1]

Bellies and Shields

How many women do you know who really like their bellies? Not very many I would guess. The women I have known—from those who are overweight to those who are very thin—are very self-conscious about their bellies. This attitude seems to be created by the culture in which we live. If we look back to the ancient, more women-centered cultures, we find statues of goddesses with big bellies and big hips. Those parts of the female body associated with child birth were emphasized in art to celebrate the importance of the ability to give birth. When you look at your (at least slightly rounded) belly, do you ever think that you look like a Goddess? In our culture, looking like a Goddess is more equated with looking like a *Playboy* centerfold. These cultural standards point out how differently women are viewed today, more as sex objects than life-givers.

A woman's belly has been referred to as "mother's mind."[2] What this means is that our instinctive sense of what is right in matters of how children are cared for and how people treat each other and the environment resides within our bellies. This is where we feel it when we see neglect and abuse. This type of knowing does not require thought, logic, rationality, or data to back it up, it is simply known to be true. In our scientific, external fact oriented culture, the knowledge of the mother's mind does not carry much weight. But it still lives within our bellies and cannot be denied.

Bellies as Drums

It is through our bellies that we receive energy from the world around us. While we have the capacity to receive and interpret many different kinds of energy from outside our bodies, our culture concentrates on only two types, light and sound energy. So we learn very early to depend on our vision and hearing as our channels of receiving information about what is happening outside us and, even then, our visual and auditory ranges are restricted to agreed upon ranges. People who are deaf or blind often find an array of other senses which can bring all kinds of information through other channels. It is not that we don't all have these ways of sensing, it is just that we have tuned them out as not important. They do not reach our conscious awareness. Just as our ear drums vibrate, matching the frequency of the sound waves which enter our ears, our bellies vibrate with the emotional energy outside us.

It is through our bellies that we receive vibrations from people around us, how they are feeling, what kind of energy they are carrying. We need to learn to pay attention to this information coming in to us, so that we are not at the mercy of the energy which surrounds us.

It is particularly important to be aware of our bellies just prior to and during Moontime. It is at this time that we become very receptive to the energy coming from outside us. All of our senses seem to be enhanced at that time which can put us on overload very easily if we are not careful. Perhaps this is why all the ancient teachings tell us to withdraw from our everyday activities at that time. Not only do we receive energy more easily at that time, but we give off energy as well. Morning Star, a Native American woman, talks about how the energy of the Moon woman is more male. She teaches that normally women's energy moves in a clockwise motion while men's energy moves counter clockwise. At the time of menstruation, women's energy shifts to a counter clockwise movement as energy is released. This is also true from a hormonal standpoint. Estrogen levels are lowest during menstruation, making women hormonally more similar to men. It is interesting to note that it is also the time when many women become less compliant and more aggressive, characteristics seen as out of character for women but normal for men.

Menstruation is a cleansing process, a monthly death and rebirth. We release the old blood to make way for the new. We release the old parts of ourselves, old patterns, to make way for growth and new ways of being. The emotion we experience at that time, if it is truly our own emotion, provides the energy for this process of renewal. Many times, however, this process is clouded by emotions we are picking up from around us. We need to protect our bellies and thus protect our natural process of renewal.

As I became more aware of my belly and the vibrations it received, I begin to understand how much I am influenced by the vibrational energy of others. Usually I am pretty good at letting other people's anger be theirs, but when I am premenstrual, I can watch their anger enter me like a black cloud and take up residence within my belly. I feel like a sponge drawing water to its center. Awareness is always the first step in change. I have become very aware of how the negative vibrations created by the visual images and sound on television are also drawn into my belly. The result of this increased receptivity is that I become depressed, angry, and sad, thinking that there is something wrong with me. How often do we hear that heightened sensitivity is a symptom of PMS. I think it would be impossible to be too sensitive to positive loving energy, or at least I cannot envision how that would be a problem. But, given that we are not surrounded by positive loving energy all the time, being too sensitive to negative energy is a problem.

Problems always present us with lessons and the lesson of this extra sensitivity is an important one. On one hand, it teaches us the need for screening or shielding our bellies when we need to. On the other hand, it heightens our awareness of the sources of negative energy in our everyday lives. Living in a negative environment, whether you are sensitive to it or not, requires energy if you are to maintain a positive state within yourself. Being "too" sensitive tells us what needs to change in our lives. For example, I am a strong supporter of the idea that there is too much violence on television, yet I used to sit and read while others in the household watched violent programs. While I was "too" sensitive, I became aware of how that vibrational energy was entering my body and changing my mood. It became intolerable. I can no longer sit in the same room with a television sending off violent vibrations.

Was I too sensitive? Should I have tried to suppress my anger at being invaded by this terrible feeling? Should I have just screened it out, allowing myself to continue my behavior unchanged? The combination of the extra sensitivity of my belly and being more in touch with mother's mind, both gifts of my impending Moontime, showed me how I was losing energy on a regular basis and that the situation was really not workable in my life. Of course, others around me (obviously not sharing the significance of my new awareness) would say that I was being too sensitive, silly, irrational and all the other adjectives normally attributed to a premenstrual woman. But no. In that moment of truth that will not sustain lies, I knew what I knew.

There are, then, two aspects to this belly sensitivity, both calling us to change. The first is the awareness of where the negative energy is and how we lose our energy to the unworkable parts of our lives. The second is how to use our extra sensitivity to open up to the higher vibrational levels, to Spirit, to the Divine energy within everything. Native people believed that just prior to and during

Moontime, the veil between our two worlds—between the physical and spiritual—becomes thinnest. At that time we can better receive information from Spirit which might guide us in our lives. This information, too, calls us to change and grow, to find new, more workable patterns in our lives.

So how do we learn to use this monthly source of transformational information—our bellies? Awareness is the first step. Think of a drum, made from an animal skin, as our bellies are covered with skin. A drum vibrates best when it is well-toned. If it is too tight the drum head does not vibrate and gives off a high, dull thud. If it is too loose it also doesn't vibrate, but gives off a low, dull thud. So our bellies must be toned through exercise and use. One awareness technique suggested by Brooke Medicine Eagle is to place a rock on your belly while you lay on the ground.[3] The belly rock should be of a medium size, round and a little concave on the bottom to fit nicely over your rounded belly. The weight of the rock both tones the muscles of your belly and draws your awareness to your belly. Brooke also teaches what she calls the belly walk. When you walk you consciously move from your belly, with the belly leading and head up. At the same time you can be visualizing a cord of light coming out from your belly and hooking on to your destination, either physical such as the end of the street or top of the hill, or non-physical such as the completion of a project. This cord of light, then, pulls you toward your goal. This type of walk is often referred to as a power walk in self-defense courses. When you walk this way you appear to be strong and powerful to others and not a good target for crime. Because, in our culture, consciousness tends to be more in our heads than in our bellies, we are more likely to walk slightly stooped over with our heads leading. Such a position limits our awareness and portrays a weak image to others.

Moving from your belly, with awareness in your belly, has other advantages also. Animals sense danger with all of their senses. An animal can tell if you are frightened, dangerous or friendly. They know this through sensing all the vibrational energy around them, visual, auditory, scent and emotion. Being in touch with the information your belly is receiving, is being in touch with your instincts so you can sense a dangerous situation. If our consciousness is only in our heads we are constantly thinking about what has happened or what might happen, thinking which blocks our awareness of what is going on around us. When our consciousness is in our bellies, we are acutely aware of the energy we are moving into so we are not surprised by what happens next.

Practice belly awareness and belly walking and feel how you are different.

Shields

While we can use our extra sensitivity to find the negative energy sources in our lives, it is also helpful to have a means of screening out this energy. Sometimes it is not always possible to change the situation we are in or to remove ourselves from it. There are also times where we must function in a negative situation while we are in Moontime. We need to make belly shields which will protect our bellies from unwanted negative energy. Since this energy is not visible, the shield itself does not need to be visible. The negative energy is, in a sense, blocked by your own energy field. Visualization constructs the energy shield and awareness holds it in place.

In visualizing a shield for your belly, you can be creative and construct a shield which is uniquely yours or you can use one of the shields suggested here. Whatever feels right to you will work the best for you. One shield which Grandmother mentioned, is one which has a mirror on the outside. It works by reflecting back the energy to its source. This is not done in a sense of sending negative energy to someone else, but more like saying this energy belongs to you and not to me. To reflect back to someone what they are putting out is a very loving thing to do, as it allows them to see themselves more clearly. To create this shield you need to close your eyes and visualize a round mirror, perhaps backed in leather, maybe with feathers hanging from it or other decorations that seem fitting to you. After you have seen this shield in your meditation, you should be able to put it in place and feel its presence with your eyes open. The shield does not need to be kept in place all the time, although it could be if you were in a particularly negative environment all the time. When you are getting close to Moontime you might want to put the shield on each morning, or you may need it only if you are going into a situation where you are not sure of the energy or know that it will be negative. It does not require your continuous awareness to maintain it, only occasional checking. The shield does not block all energy, only that which is not beneficial to you.

There are many other types of shields which can be used. One is surrounding yourself with white light. Visualizing a white light, like an egg shell around you, initially while you are meditating and later with your eyes open, is a very peaceful shield. If you are aware of your aura and know its color, imagine your aura becoming very dense and extending farther out from your body to act as a shield. Sometimes this can initially be done in meditation by picturing yourself looking into a mirror where you see your own image with your aura around it. See the aura in the mirror image becoming brighter, larger, and denser.

There are also more traditional shields, such as those used by Native American or African warriors. These were generally constructed out of hide or wood and were painted with symbols of power. It is fun to imagine such a shield for yourself, putting your own symbols of power on it. One very powerful way to think of placing these symbols on your shield is with menstrual blood. Moon blood represents the power of women and is very appropriate for a belly shield to be used around Moontime. Play with these ideas until you have a shield that feels right to you and then practice using it.

One way to make your shield seem more real to you is to actually construct a shield. There are many ways to do this. You can simply draw the shield on paper, frame it, and hang it in your bedroom or over your personal altar. If your shield is a mirror, you could get a round mirror and decorate it with leather and feathers or however you imagine your shield. A shield could also be constructed of leather or hide stretched over a wooden or metal hoop on which you can paint your symbols of power (using your own Moon blood if you like). Having a physical representation of your shield can help you remember to use it and can also serve as a reminder of your commitment to use your Moontime well.

Removing Negative Energy

There are times when even the best of shields don't get put up quickly enough or when you don't anticipate needing one. When you are caught with your shield down and the negative energy has entered your body, filling you with gloom or anger, the sooner you process it out the better. Moving the energy out of your body can be accomplished through visualization and breathing. You will need to find a place to sit quietly and close your eyes. Breathe in through your belly and then as you breathe out imagine yourself as a tree sending a long tap root down into the Earth. Breathe in again through your belly. As you exhale, send branches and leaves out the top of your head to the sky. Breathe in again and send any negative energy down through your root to the Mother Earth for recycling. Breathe in the Mother's loving energy through your root and then breathe out the negative energy through your leaves releasing it to Father Sky for reprocessing. Breathe in through your leaves the loving energy of the Sky Father and then exhale to release any negative energy again through your roots. Continue this circular breathing pattern until you feel that the negative energy is gone and you are filled with the loving energy of Earth and Sky.

This type of breathing is useful to gain energy whenever you feel a low energy level. It is also a grounding exercise that can help when you feel too spacey or ungrounded.

There is another breathing pattern which can be useful to use in situations where you feel negative energy coming to you. Of course, as soon as you recognize that you have been caught with your shield down, you should immediately visualize your shield in place.

Then you can think of breathing in good energy through your belly and then breathing out any negativity through your heart directly back to the person from whom the negativity came. By sending it out through your heart, your intention is to return this person's energy with love. This type of breathing can be done with minimal awareness on your part so that you can maintain a conversation if you must.

Other cleansing processes might use water, such as a shower or bath. This is particularly effective if you add sea salt to the bath water or rub it on your skin in the shower. Smoke from herbs such as sage and cedar will cleanse negative energy, while sweetgrass smoke draws the positive. Waft the smoke over your body while visualizing the release of negative energy. Some kinds of music are particularly cleansing of negative energy. Experiment and find some music that seems to lift you up and make you feel light and good.

The Shield of Space

Taking time just before and during Moontime to be by yourself, where you do not need a belly shield is important. In a sense, the space you put between yourself and others serves as a shield for negative energy. It is important to have this time when you do not have to use your energy to maintain a shield, where you can be completely open to the higher energy available to you at that time. Creating a place which is filled with good energy and beauty is helpful. Each time you use this place, whether it is your bedroom, a spot out in nature, or some other room in your house, clear the energy through some cleansing ritual. Light incense, burn sage, cedar, or sweetgrass, light a candle, say prayers, ask for all that is not beneficial to you to leave, or use whatever method you find effective to cleanse an area. Within this space create a Moon altar, a place to keep things which are special to you, things which signify your relation to the Moon's cycles and other cycles of nature. If your place is outdoors you may want to keep a special bag with these things in it to take with you to that spot. We will talk more about the creation of special space for honoring your Moontime, but the general idea is to have a space which is itself a shield from your everyday life and the people around you. While most of us cannot realistically retreat for four days, even a small amount of time spent in this way will help to make good use of our power of sensitivity.

6

Emotions as Teachers

The Sacred Mountain

They watched the water in the stream flow past making little ripples in places and smoothing out in others.

"There are many teachers we have talked of, both those outside us and those inside us, but there is one teacher that is probably the most important of all—emotion."

"Why is that, Grandmother?"

"E-motion means to put into motion and that is what our emotions do for us. They motivate us to take action and learn our lessons. We need to learn a little more of their purpose or we might end up engaging in the wrong action, action which is not healthy for us. For example, negative emotions—anger, sadness, fear—do not feel good when we have them, so sometimes we do just any old thing to try to stop them, the sooner the better. This is very similar to taking a pain pill if you have a pain in your body. If you don't bother to find out what the pain is all about, it will just come back or you may even have made it worse."

"Do you mean like when you are angry at someone and you yell at them, it might make you feel better right then but it usually doesn't solve the problem?"

"Yes, that is a good example, but it needs to be taken a step further. Not only have you not solved the problem, but you don't even know what the problem is. If something that someone says or does has the capacity to trigger our anger it is simply showing us an area of ourselves where more learning needs to take place. Other people are like mirrors for us and in them we can see ourselves clearly — even the parts of ourselves which we deny, don't like, or need further development. When we see in other people these parts of ourselves with which we have not identified, we become angry."

"Let me see if I understand this. If I become angry with someone because they are acting very selfish, does that mean that I'm selfish?"

"It could be, but not necessarily. If a person is acting selfish, that means they are taking care of their own needs, perhaps to the extreme and in an unbalanced way. It probably would reflect to the part of you that doesn't take care of your own needs. Maybe you learned that putting yourself first was selfish, so you rejected that, and now you put everyone else's needs before yours and yours never get met. So you think maybe other people should be meeting your needs since you're not taking care of them yourself. Seeing someone who meets their own needs gives you a clear picture of what you have neglected in yourself and the anger calls your attention to it. Anger says, 'Look closer, my dear, there is something of importance here!'"

"Oh my, that example sure hit home! But what about sadness, we don't feel that toward others?"

"Any negative emotion can be thought of as a messenger from our deeper self. It says pay attention and then, because it is uncomfortable, it motivates us to learn the lesson which is attached to it. If we try to avoid learning the lesson, it just comes up again in a different, perhaps even less tolerable form. Sadness is often a lesson about loss. We experience loss daily as a part of living. Each moment passes away never to be relived again. Generally we are not overly attached to moments so we don't experience much sadness about this. But when we are attached to something—that is we have identified with it rather than our true selves—we experience sadness when we lose it or think of losing it. We all experience this emotion to some degree because we all are attached to the physical, while that is not who we really are. Sadness always calls us to remember that we are spiritual beings and, in that realm, there is no loss. For example, perhaps I am sad because I am old and wrinkled. I have lost the beauty of my youth. The sadness calls me to know that I am much more that I appear in my physical body. The skin of my spirit body is forever beautiful and that is who I really am."

"Oh Grandmother, I know that is true. You are very beautiful to me."

"Thank you, Dawn. That is always nice to hear, even though I know it to be true deep within me. We also need to talk of fear. What lessons does it hold for us?"

"When I am fearful of something, I know I certainly pay attention to it."

"Yes, fear can be a very important emotion which mobilizes the whole body to respond to a dangerous situation. But many times we experience fear, perceiving a dangerous situation, when there is no danger. This is the type of fear that we are talking about here."

"You mean like fear of talking in front of a group or walking in the woods at night."

"That's right. Neither of those situations is dangerous. Fear here is calling us to see how it restricts us and keeps us from being all that we can be. The opposite of fear is trust, trust in ourselves, in spirit, in the universe. If we really trust our intuition rather than letting our minds run away with us, we will know if a situation is really dangerous or if it is only our mind telling us it is. Why would the woods be dangerous at night? Perhaps, you think, because you cannot see around you. There are many ways to see and intuition is one of them."

"So how do you deal with fear?"

"You center yourself, check your intuition for real danger, and then walk through it. Fear goes away when we confront those areas with trust. Sometimes we need to approach our fears in small steps and sometimes it is best to jump right in, either way fear calls us to trust and to wholeness."

"And what about the positive emotions of joy, happiness, and love, Grandmother?"

"Those are the feelings which tell us we are learning our lessons well. They come to say, 'Well done, keep up the good work, you're on the right track' and things like that. They don't last too long because there is always more work to do. In many ways, walking your path through life is like climbing up the Sacred Mountain. It stands white and snow capped in the sunlight and is admired by all who stand on the plains. Some people are satisfied with living their whole life on the plains because trying to reach that mountain would be too much work. Those who begin the journey climb the first rise and stand on top feeling wonderful that they have gotten a little closer. They stay there for a little while and then begin the descent into the valley before the next slightly higher foothill. As they go down into the valley they lose sight of the sacred mountain and become lost in the trees. They wander around looking for the path experiencing anger, sadness, and fear. As they learn the lessons of these emotions they find the path again and climb to the next peak. When they arrive they are joyful, happy, peaceful, and loving and they can see so much farther than they could before. They stay for a short time and then begin the descent into the valley before the next higher peak. And the cycle repeats. Our peak experience lets us know that we are, indeed, getting closer to the sacred mountain and, yet, there are times we wander in the valley lost, doubting whether the sacred mountain even exists. Some people try to stay too long on a peak because they want the positive emotions to stay forever. When they do that they stop growing and become stagnant. They don't feel good anymore even on the peak. While those points of clarity are very important in our lives, we must always continue with the journey. After a while it is possible to maintain a sense of peacefulness even in the valleys, because you have come to trust the process and know the next peak is not too far away."

"It feels good just to think of it this way and to know that it is a continuing cycle. Sometimes when I have a negative emotion it feels like it will last forever. It helps to know that there is a lesson there and that it won't last forever."

"Using your journal to track your emotions and explore the lessons is a good way to get a perspective on this cycle of change. Mother Earth teaches us of the continuous cycles of change through her seasons of growth and quiet. This song is about the great wheel of change which runs through our lives:

"I am seed in the East, growing soft green stems
I am seed in the East, growing soft green stems
I am flower in the South, brightly colored many
    shades,
I am flower in the South, brightly colored many
    shades.
I am fruit in the West, growing seed deep within,
I am fruit in the West, growing seed deep within.
I am dry in the North waiting for my release,
I am silent in the North waiting for my release."[1]

Emotions—"Keep them under control!"

Even the word emotion creates emotion within us. In a culture where emotion is considered to be dangerously close to mental illness, emotion is something to keep under control. The emotions that women appear to experience most frequently—fear, sadness, depression—are generally dealt with as psychological disturbances, while the main emotion which men experience—anger—is often not seen as abnormal, but if it is, it is dealt with in the legal system. This is not to say that women do not experience anger or that men do not experience fear, it is just that our social rules allow men to be angry but not fearful and women to be fearful but not angry. Men's fear often looks like anger to us and women's anger often takes the form of anxiety or depression. So our emotions are expressed in socially acceptable ways for each gender and too much expression is viewed as deviant. When we speak of someone who is emotionally "healthy," we are often referring to a person who keeps their emotions well under control and whose mood does not vary much from day to day and month to month, nothing bothers them too much, and, if they are female, they don't make waves. They do what is expected of them by others.

The problem with this cultural view of emotion and emotional health is that there is no acknowledgment of emotion as a teacher. Emotion is to be controlled, managed, or gotten rid of. Even positive emotion cannot be experienced freely, as it is seen as deviant, allowed only for short periods of time and seen as something that should be toned down. When we experience emotion, we are being activated, given a burst of energy. Emotion also captures our attention and focuses it on a lesson. Negative emotions in particular provide us with an optimal learning opportunity, supplying the motivation, attention and focus for new awareness and growth. Because being emotional is often identified with the feminine, there is a need to re-claim the status of emotion as the powerful teacher that it is. This is important for men as well as for women. To relegate this source of growth and transformation to the status of "to be controlled" or "to be suppressed" is to lose a major source of self-knowledge.

How Emotions Teach

In many ancient teachings both Eastern and Western, there is a lesson about mirrors. It says that everyone and everything in the Circle of life is a mirror which reflects the parts of ourselves we need to see. This is similar to the Jungian notion of projection. We project our Shadow, the undeveloped, unconscious parts of ourselves, onto others. Thus, when we become angry with others, we are really angry with a part of ourselves which we do not accept. When we admire another person, we are seeing a part of ourselves which needs to be better developed. Rather than being judgmental of others, we need to see these projections as paths to our own Shadow, shedding light on those darkened parts of ourselves which need to be accepted into the whole of our being.

All emotions we feel toward others call us to look at ourselves. Not to blame ourselves, but to look at ourselves. Some people interpret this as making yourself responsible for everything in a blaming way. For example, if a woman is being abused and she is angry at her abuser, does that mean she should be angry with herself? Not exactly. The anger is pointing out to her how something in her needs to change in order for this abuse to stop. It is unlikely that it will stop simply because she is angry with the abuser. So yes, in one sense, the anger with herself will motivate her to make a change in herself which is very difficult to make and probably would not occur without the presence of anger. In this case the anger provides the energy and insists that the situation is intolerable. If the anger is directed at the abuser, it is wasted. If the anger is allowed to reflect the path to change within the woman, it is energy well spent.

Guilt and blame are not constructive parts of this process, in fact, they obstruct the process. Self-knowledge is not bad. Finding out that you have areas where you need to grow is very important. We do not need to feel guilty about this or blame ourselves for having a shadow. This is part of the human condition and our growth process. We see our Shadow in others and they see theirs in us. Taking responsibility for our own Shadow, our own growth process, does not involve blame.

In the previous chapter we discussed how important it is to be sure that an emotion is yours before you begin to work with it. Women in general are pretty good at receiving the reflections of their own emotions, but they are also good at receiving other people's emotions and not reflecting them back. This often leads to them to blame themselves for other people's negative emotions. Learning to distinguish between your own and other people's emotion allows you to learn how to reflect back to others their own shadow projections, allowing them to see themselves more clearly. It also insures that you are working with emotional material which originates within you, as you begin to shed light on your own darkness. This is, of course, particularly important around Moontime when your receptivity to all emotion is high.

To understand the various emotions as teachers, we will look at each one and the special knowledge it brings. We begin with awareness of our emotions and then proceed to work with the emotion to discover its lesson.

Anger

Much has been written in the self-help and psychological literature about anger and how to get rid of it. It seems that we are not supposed to be angry. Women are becoming aware of how angry they are and new theories suggest that anger from the loss of self and voice, which often happens in this culture, is the source of depression.[2] Emily Martin, writing about Premenstrual Syndrome and anger says, "In order for women to see their rage as a blessing rather than a curse, it may be necessary for women to feel that their rage is legitimate."[3] Female Jungian analysts feel that some of this anger is part of the collective unconscious (the shared consciousness of women over our ancestral past) created by women living under patriarchy and suppression for centuries. Some anger is a shared experience among women, a conflict between what we know to be true and how we are experiencing ourselves in the current culture.

When we become angry with abusive situations, that anger reflects back to the strong woman who lives in our Shadow, the one who does not tolerate a lack of respect for life, for women, for children. She wants to be acknowledged as a part of us who needs expression. The expression of anger is not important for dissipating the energy. While releasing anger may feel good for the moment, it does not move you toward resolution of the conflict within. In a way, releasing anger takes away the motivation to change. So this woman who is angry at the culture and needs expression will not be placated by beating on pillows or screaming at the top of her lungs. She wants action, she wants change. She doesn't want to have to be angry anymore.

The energy which anger provides us with, along with the knowledge of what must change within us, opens the door for change. We don't always step through that door, because the change we need to make is usually something we were hoping that we wouldn't have to do.

When we have trigger points for anger, where one little thing happens and we react in a way that is not appropriate for what happened, there is usually a very important lesson to be learned and one which we have been avoiding for a long time. Of course we can't learn all our lessons at once and therefore it is only natural to put some on hold. It is helpful, I think, to know that for every trigger point we have, there is a lesson waiting. Sometimes this helps me to take the focus off the person who has triggered me. Many triggers reveal patterns we have had for a long time which deny parts of ourselves or the truth which lives within. Triggers are rich tools for the exploration of Shadow.

One difficulty of exploring anger is learning to leave blame and guilt behind. Taking responsibility for your own anger simply means that no one can make you angry. It is a choice you make somewhere deep within you, which depends on your past history. Two people could have the same thing happen to them and one might get angry and the other not. Clearly the determining factor, then, is the person not the event. To say that you are *responsible* for your anger means that you have the *ability to respond* to your anger, you are response-able. It does not imply blame or guilt. If you were not responsible for your emotion, and someone else was, you would be at the complete mercy of others as to how you felt.

95

The most freeing aspect of this idea, that I am responsible for my own anger, is that I am not responsible for anyone else's anger. I don't need to be worried about making someone else angry. They choose whether they will be angry about what I have done. That doesn't mean that I can just run around and do anything I please to other people. I always need to move from my own truth to the best of my ability at any given time. This is part of the law of good relationship, that I be in good relationship with all that is. But it doesn't mean I am responsible for the anger of others.

Being responsible for my own anger means that I can choose whether I want to use the lesson of that anger or put it on hold. If I put it on hold, I know that it will not go away, but will return periodically until I choose to deal with it. If I choose to learn the lesson then I must face the change which it brings. Sometimes I get part way through the process and decide I don't want to make that change now. I become aware of the change needed and decide to do it another time. When it comes back, I still have the awareness and I am closer to making the change.

There are many ways to work with anger. The first step involves bringing the anger back into yourself to find the source. Usually when we become angry, we project the anger outward toward someone or something else. Bringing it back into yourself begins the process of awareness, the process of looking for the lesson. Use the energy of your anger to write in your journal, to paint or draw, to dance, or anything which brings you into closer alignment with your hidden inner world. Working with nature at this time is also helpful. Ritual work is often useful, where symbolic actions are taken to open yourself up to new possibilities. One ritual is digging a hole in the Earth and speaking your anger into it, putting in a seed, and covering it up. The anger acts as a fertilizer for the seed which represents the new growth which will come from it. The act of speaking your anger out loud helps you to get in touch with the source of the anger. Another ritual is taking a stone which will fit in the palm of your right hand and sitting with the stone, sending all your anger and everything which relates to it into the stone. This can be done by consciously thinking it into the stone or by speaking it out loud. When you think you have every-thing in the stone, throw it into a stream or bury it in the ground so the stone may return this anger to Mother Earth for recycling. By clearing the anger away you have opened a space for the new awareness and lesson. Another ritual which works well is to sit with your back against a tree, visualize your anger moving into the tree and being replaced by good energy and infinite possibilities of the Earth and sky vibrations which meet in the tree. The possibili-ties for ritual work with anger are endless: smudging (allowing the smoke of sage, cedar or sweetgrass flow over you), lighting a candle, working with crystals, meditating with plants, a prayer for seeing in a new way. What they all have in common is a focused intention to clear away the anger so that you may become aware of its source and the new knowledge which awaits there.

Working with anger in this way is not something which is done once. Rituals must be repeated. Since we live in a microwave, push-button, pill-popping world, we think that this work should be easier. I think that's why we so often merely project anger on to others, suppress it or try to pretend it doesn't exist. Perhaps we don't realize how much of our energy this denial takes. Working with anger is hard and difficult work, but repressing it is even harder. Writing in a journal, paying attention to your dreams, medi-tating on it, doing rituals to move the energy in a symbolic way, focusing your intention on the process—all of these must be done consistently to move you to a new level of understanding. It is also important to have support for the work. Sometimes a partner will be supportive of the process, a good friend, or maybe a women's Circle. A therapist might also help support the process and pro-vide feedback which allows you to see yourself better.

Anger is a powerful teacher for women. It will not let us rest until that warrior woman residing in our shadow begins to walk in the light. She uses the soft power of love to enforce the law of good relationship, the deep understanding of all women about the respect for all things.

Fear

It has been suggested by a number of women authors, and I certainly have observed in myself and other women, that we share a collective fear as women. Whether we see this as coming from previous lives of persecution, from our mothers, grandmothers, and great grandmothers through generations, or from the socialization process we have endured in this lifetime, does not really matter. The most common fears of women are: being crazy, not being good enough, being overpowered and hurt (physically, sexually, verbally, emotionally), loneliness, having our children taken from us, not being able to take care of ourselves financially.

These fears are not as neurotic as many psychologists would have us believe. Women who spoke their own mind in the 1930s through the 1950s were given hysterectomies to "calm them down." Women are currently prescribed various psychoactive drugs to mask the effects of living in situations that inner warrior women say are intolerable. Women are beaten, raped, verbally and emotionally abused in their own homes, in the work place, and on the street. Women are isolated from supportive relationships. Almost every mother I know who endured the process of divorce has been threatened with the loss of her children by an angry husband. Women's incomes remain far lower than those of men with the same training and qualifications. Indeed, women have fewer opportunities to get training and qualifications. Are we neurotic then, that we have these fears? I think not! But fear, regardless of its source calls us to learn. It asks us to be aware of the source and to find new ways to respond to the old triggers.

One of the interesting things about fear is that, as an emotion, it does not respond well to your thinking. For example, you might know that you have been a good mother and have a good relationship with your kids, but when your soon-to-be ex-husband says that you are a rotten mother who abandoned her children because you left the kids one night a week to go to aerobics class, fear wells up and you panic. If another woman told you that story, you would tell her to tell her husband to get real. Such fear we have of not being able to protect our children! Another example: you might know that you have always done a good job at work, but when the boss wants to talk to you about your performance, you panic. We have a fear of not meeting the expectations of others.

The reason fear is so resistant to our rational thoughts is that fear was probably laid down in our brains much earlier than our ability to think rationally. If our mothers could not protect us when we were young children, should we not also fear being able to protect our own children? If we were criticized for being ourselves and saying what we knew rather than meeting other's expectations when we were children, why would we feel that being ourselves now will bring acceptance? Whatever we think we know from an adult perspective, when we fear, we feel from the child's perspective.

Understanding where our fear comes from helps us to deal with it more effectively. The fearful child, who feels helpless and ineffective in influencing her world, lives within us all. We need to reassure her, protect her, love her, and listen to her. As adults we can discriminate whether danger really exists or whether it is the child who is frightened. One way to do this is to look in the mirror and see your reflection as your best friend. If she were in the situation that you find yourself in, what would you tell her? You could also do this in your journal by writing a letter to a best friend who is in your situation. What this technique does is move you to a place where you can more objectively assess the real danger in a situation and separate from the emotional triggers of the child. If you cannot do a reality check for yourself, you might have a friend you can run it by, but realize that your friend may respond, in part, from her child.

Once you have determined that there is no real danger, or, if there is, you have realistically planned for it, you move forward into the fear in whatever size steps you can handle. Fear is anticipatory. Once you have faced the fear and moved through it, fear is left behind. Fear brings our attention to the parts of ourselves which need healing, often the small, fearful child within. The child heals when we acknowledge her fear, reassure her that we will protect her, and confront the situation as an adult. In facing fear and healing it, we learn our inner strength.

Sadness

Sadness is commonly experienced by women prior to and during Moontime. Women often report crying easily and general feelings of sadness for apparently no reason. In one sense, it is an emotion which is very appropriate at that time. Within the body's cycle, it is a time when an egg has not been fertilized and the body is preparing to let go of the nest it had prepared for it. In a real sense it represents the loss of a possible child. In a more symbolic sense it represents a time of letting go of things, perhaps things that are no longer needed or possibilities which will not be realized, a cleansing to make room for new growth. Mourning our losses, those things which we need to let go of, is a natural process and just prior to or during Moontime is our natural time to do this.

Another contributor to our sad feelings at that time is our increased awareness of our connection as women to the Earth and to all other women. At a time when the Earth and women are being exploited and abused, we feel their pain as well as our own. We also feel the pain of the children, as we are so in touch with "mothers mind." In one psychological theory, this overwhelming feeling of sadness has been called cosmic sadness, sadness which comes through our connection to all things. There are women, men, and children all over the Earth who are starving and suffering from abuse and war. Is it surprising that we feel their pain at a time when we are extra sensitive and tuned into our connection to all the Circle of life?

While it is not always very practical for us to go around crying when we need to go to work and do other daily tasks, it is important to give ourselves time to feel the sadness, to acknowledge it. Cry for the children, for the people, for the Earth. Crying is healing. There is a wonderful song about crying which was given to my friend Sue St. Pierre by the beaver:

Bitter sweet tears rolling down warm cheeks
Glisten in the Moonlight, glisten in the firelight.
Quick silver flowing from inside the soul
Glisten in the Moonlight, glisten in the firelight.

Chorus:

Tears of laughter, tears of pain, we shall cry together
   without shame.
We shall give away these sacred tears.
May on a key, May on a key, Yolly Yolly Yo
We shall give away these sacred tears.

River flowing, a river of tears
Don't dam the feeling flowing in your heart.
Don't wipe them away, please stand and pray
Say the feelings flowing in your heart.
Tears are not weak when you're feeling strong
Strong with the feelings flowing in your heart.*(Chorus)*

Circle of Sisters with hearts that pound
Standing together on sacred ground
Tears so pure they will cleanse the soul
We shall sanctify this holy ground
Tears for our children and our own lost souls
We shall build a dream on sacred ground. *(Chorus)*[4]

Women cry for many reasons, sadness is just one of them. We also cry when we are very angry, when we are hurt, because we feel happy, essentially, whenever we feel things very strongly. The ability to feel things very deeply is so important, but it is also important not to get lost in the feeling. Sadness is to be experienced, losses are to be grieved, but we are far more than our sadness and losses. They teach us on a body level, what is not working in our lives, what is not working in the world. They teach us that loss is part of a natural cycle of growth. They are fine teachers and we need to honor them with our tears and learn from them. With the knowledge of our deep feelings which we gain from our Moontime, we become strong as we move back into the world to speak the truth we have found.

Ecstasy

This is a feeling which we don't hear too much about and is often described as happiness or joy. Ecstasy is more like intense happiness, total joy, a feeling of supreme well-being, knowledge of complete oneness. These positive emotions tell us that we are on the right track. They arise when we are centered, that is, when body, mind, and spirit are one. This may occur in a moment when we see our wholeness reflected to us through others, it may be when we feel the connection to all things through nature, or it might be when we are in a relationship which balances us. Ecstasy says, "This is what wholeness feels like. This is what it feels like to know that you are both one person and the whole universe at the same time." We get glimpses of ecstasy from time to time as we work our way toward wholeness.

Many women are afraid of feeling good. Perhaps it stems from a childhood where feeling good was not allowed, a relationship where they were expected to match the feelings of their partner whether they felt that way or not, too many years of suppressing all feelings, or the idea that if they feel good they tempt fate and somehow something bad will happen. We need to trust these good feelings and allow them to teach us about wholeness. It is OK for us to be feeling good even though things might not be good for everyone around us. When I was speaking to a group of young people about my experiences with vision questing and encouraging them to go out and sit in nature for a day, one young woman came to speak to me afterward. She said that there was a place in the woods where she used to go as a child to be with the trees but it is polluted now and when she goes there she just cries. I explained to her that the trees still live there and appreciate her tears, but that they have much more to say to her. The land there has much to teach her about oneness and wholeness, and that after she had offered her tears, she should listen deeply to their teachings. If we become lost in the sadness, we can miss the message about the joy of connection.

A Native American teacher, Amy Lee, has suggested that some of the songs which we sing about the Earth and our connection to all of life need healing. While experiencing sadness about the loss of trees and species is very important information, we need to move beyond the sadness to action. An example is a song which I have heard many times called Ancient Mother:

> Ancient Mother, I hear you calling, Ancient Mother, I
> hear your song.
> Ancient Mother, I feel your laughter, Ancient Mother, I
> taste your tears.

Amy Lee's healing version of this song is:

> Ancient Mother, I heed your calling, Ancient Mother, I
> sing your song.
> Ancient Mother, I share your laughter, Ancient Mother
> I dry your tears.[5]

Allowing ourselves to experience joy as well as sadness leads to the passion which moves us into action in our lives.

Honoring the Teachings

Each emotion we experience holds a lesson to be learned now or later. To honor our emotions as teachers we need to record the teachings. After taking some time to be with your emotions and using some of the rituals described here, write in your journal about the feelings and the knowledge you have gained from them. Writing and reflecting help you to get a sense of your journey. If women did this on every Moontime, think of how wise we each would be by the time we reach menopause. Seeing our greater emotionality at Moontime as an open door to wisdom helps us to feel good about being a woman who cycles. I have an image of a woman warrior, dancing her spiral dance, circling ever upward into wisdom as she moves her feet in time to the heart beat of Mother Earth.

7

Awakening to Beauty

The Basket

As she reached for another willow branch, Grandmother saw Dawn and her friend, Rose, approaching.

"What are you doing, Grandmother?" asked Dawn.

"I'm weaving a willow basket for carrying herbs. Do you like it?"

"It's beautiful!" both girls said at once.

"It seems too nice to use just for carrying herbs" said Dawn, examining the intricately twisted branches of green willow and red dogwood.

"Nothing would be too beautiful for gathering herbs. Sometimes we think that beautiful things should be reserved only for special times and places. Even with ourselves, we act in a beautiful way only on certain occasions. The Beauty Way, however, tells us of the importance of walking in beauty at all times."

"Do you mean that I should wear my most beautiful clothes everyday?" said Dawn, not quite believing what she was hearing.

"Not if you mean physical clothes. We can, however, dress ourselves in the beauty of who we are in every moment."

"I'm not sure I understand that," Rose chimed in.

"There is a song which says 'May I walk a Beauty Path with every step I take and may I speak the Beauty Way with every word I make.' One of the meanings of this song is that in every moment we wish to create beauty around us. How do you think we could do that?"

"Maybe it means being nice to the people and things you meet along the way. That would be beautiful," said Dawn.

"Or it might mean picking up trash or not polluting the Earth as you go throughout your day," added Rose.

"It means both of those things and much more. Let me tell you a little about the Beauty Way. In order for you to create beauty around you, you must be beautiful inside. This, of course, is easier said than done. To be beautiful inside you need to love and honor all parts of yourself. Some of these parts would be your physical body, your emotional self, your intellect and intuition, your higher Self or connection to Spirit, and your inner male and female. You see we have many parts to us which need to be explored, loved and honored. This is a process which goes on through out your life as you learn more and more about your beauty. By knowing that your beauty comes from inside, you have plenty to spill over everything you come into contact with. You can give your beauty away."

"I'm not sure I understand that on a practical level," said Dawn. "We have talked a lot about how we can use nature, other people, dreams, meditation, and emotions as ways to know yourself and to make yourself whole. But how does this relate to others? How would I know if I were creating beauty around me?"

"I know this is a little abstract. Let's see if we can use some specific examples. On a physical level, creating beauty means taking care of yourself physically. Developing your ability to listen to the needs of your body - what it needs for fuel, when it needs to rest, exercising it, and treating it in a loving way. This means on a practical level that you eat to feed your body for health as well as for pleasure, that you don't let the many things you have to do override your body's need to rest and replenish itself, that you do regular exercise to keep your muscles and belly toned so they may support your work, and that you take the time to dress neatly and groom your body just as you would tend a garden of beautiful flowers. It is important, also, on a physical level to know that disease is a situation where something is out of balance. It may be created on a physical level, such as incorrect diet, or it could stem from emotional or spiritual issues, but usually it represents a block in the free flow of energy through your system and, thus, an imbalance. So staying healthy on a physical level is the first step in being beautiful inside."

"Well, I certainly feel more beautiful when I take care of myself physically and stay healthy," said Dawn thoughtfully.

"Then, of course, there is also beauty on an emotional level. While perhaps the ideal here is an inner peacefulness as beauty, it is rarely achieved on a continuous basis. It is more likely that our beauty will come from taking personal responsibility for our own emotions and allowing others to take responsibility for their own emotions. Even this is difficult to do but using your emotions as powerful teachers is an important part of walking the Beauty Way.

"Another way in which we create beauty is through honoring our inner truth. This means that we must walk it and talk it. Speaking what you know to be true even when others are not receptive is difficult, while walking your truth - that is behaving in ways consistent with it - is even harder."

"That's the truth!" Dawn laughed.

"None of us come close to being perfect on this one, but it is important to recognize the ways in which our beliefs or truths are not being honored by our action.

"It is also important to honor the beauty which surrounds us. Taking the time to tell a flower just how beautiful it is, thanking the breeze for its gentle touch, saying hello to the sun and the Moon each day. Recognizing the beauty that exists in other people and in everything that is. All of these things are part of walking a Beauty Path."

"What about the basket you are making, is that also part of the Beauty Path?"

"Creating beauty in all you do right down to the smallest thing is part of this path. Whether you are preparing food, creating something, providing a service, or supervising people, doing it in a beautiful way means acting with respect for whoever or whatever you are working with. It also means making things nice to look at, and beautiful to touch and hear. As I weave these branches I sing a song of respect and gratefulness for willow. I am making the basket beautiful for carrying the wonderful herbs I gather for healing. Creating beauty in this way means really being there in each moment, being aware and paying attention to what you are doing and what surrounds you."

"That seems so hard to do! I try to remember everything but I forget or I get caught up in thinking about the past or future and don't pay attention to what I am doing."

"It is very difficult to stay joyfully in the moment. No one can do this continuously, but it is a lesson we all must work on. Even doing it a little will create more beauty in our own lives, which can then be shared with all that surrounds us. The song I mentioned before helps us to remember to create beauty in each moment of our lives.

"May I walk the Beauty Path with every step I take
And may I speak the Beauty Way with every word I
   make
Way ah hey, way ah hey, way ah hey oh
Way ah hey, way ah hey, way ah hey oh
May I dance the Beauty Path with every step I take
And may I sing the Beauty Way with every word I
   make
Way ah hey, way ah hey, way ah hey oh
Way ah hey, way ah hey, way ah hey oh."[1]

What Is Beauty?

Beauty is a word that seems to have a very limited meaning when applied to women in our culture. The whole beauty industry developed to help women conform to physical standards which men find pleasing and sexually arousing. The saying, "Beauty is only skin deep" refers to this narrow definition of beauty. In Webster's dictionary beauty is defined as "the quality present in a person or thing that gives intense aesthetic pleasure or deep satisfaction to the mind or the senses." Beautiful is defined as "excellent of its kind, wonderful, remarkable." Beauty in its more inclusive form is something which exists within a person and is experienced in a positive way both by themselves and others around them. Another way of saying it is that, in developing your beauty, you become your best and truest self. When you become your best and truest self, you also become highly attractive to other people, but this is only a by-product of the process, not the goal.

Beauty on a Physical Level

Beauty on a physical level, by our more expanded definition, is taking care of your body in such a way that you allow it to function most efficiently. If you view your body as the temple which houses your spirit, the body must be treated with great respect. Your body connects you to the Earth and Earth knowledge, while spirit connects us to the energy of the Creator and the universe. For us to be who we really are, both physical and spiritual must be honored. Mind and emotion are, in a sense, the interface between the physical and spiritual, they are the messengers, the communication system. Rather than seeing this all as part of a functioning whole, we sometimes get things disconnected and separated. This leads to a situation where we eat or drink in response to anger or depression rather than seeing those emotions as communication from our spirit about our learning. Eating and drinking make the body feel good momentarily and also make it easier to ignore the calling of our spirit. Then after the effects of the food or drink wear off, we are again left with ourselves and the same lessons we had before, which lead to more anger or depression. Thus, if the emotions and physical body get separated off from our spiritual self, we do not realize our beauty. At the risk of creating an artificial sense of separation among the parts of ourselves, we will look at creating beauty on a physical, emotional, and spiritual level separately and then come back to talk about their integration.

Eating

How often have we heard the saying, "You are what you eat?" Does that mean that if you eat beauty you will become beautiful? Maybe. Eating is one thing that affects how efficiently our bodies work. If we overload our bodies with fat, salt, sugar, and too much protein (the standard American diet), it is clear that, not only do our bodies not work efficiently, but they become diseased. The recent research on diet has shown that cancer in women and osteoporosis is related to a diet rich in dairy products, protein from meat, and fat. Even with the advanced medical care in our country, we have the highest incidence in the world for breast cancer, ovarian cancer, and osteoporosis. Women in China who eat very little meat protein or fat and drink no milk have the lowest rates of these diseases. Initially, researchers thought that it might be race which affected the rates, but they have since found that Chinese women who have moved to this country and begun to eat the American diet, have increased incidence of these diseases which approximates that of women growing up in this country.

There is much good research on diet and health but it takes a long time to change ingrained eating habits encouraged by the powerful meat and dairy industry lobbies or to affect the health care system or change public policy.[2] In addition to disease, the more subtle effects of our high fat diet comes from its effect on menstruation. A high percentage of body fat leads to earlier onset of menstruation. Again we can see the comparison between Western countries, where the age of menarche has decreased from 16 years to 12.5 years over the last 100 years, and other countries where the diet is lower in fat and menarche is later. An additional problem is the estrogen which is added to the feed of beef cattle and makes its way into our bodies. In countries such as Mexico, where there are few regulations on hormones fed to cattle to increase growth, girls as young as five years have menstruated and young boys have developed breasts. While our country has more regulations, hormones are still used to the extent that many European countries will not import our beef. This increased estrogen in our diets can affect not only the onset of menstruation, but also may cause, or at least feed, cancer within the female reproductive system.

Other foods we consume which have been linked to menstrual irregularities and PMS are sugar, caffeine, alcohol, and salt. Two hundred years ago the average person in affluent countries consumed less than two pounds of sugar a year. Today the average person in the Western world consumes over two pounds per week, much of which is hidden in highly processed foods, junk food, and fast food. Caffeine, alcohol and salt addictions are rather common in this country and contribute in a variety of ways to the symptoms women experience with PMS.

The use of pesticides, hormones, and artificial fertilizers makes eating in a healthy way more of a challenge than we may realize. In her book on nutrition and menstrual health, Linda Ojeda says, "By the time food reaches the dinner table, it has lost an estimated 50% of its nutrients. The remainder of the vitamins and minerals we ourselves destroy in preparation."[3] A 1980 USDA survey showed that women get only 50% to 75% of the recommended daily allowances of thiamin, niacin, calcium, vitamin B6, magnesium, and iron. This is primarily due to the increased consumption of highly processed, nutrient deficient foods. The percentage of processed foods included in the American diet in 1940 was 10% and in 1980 was 50%. Over the same time there was a 50% increase in simple sugars and a 54% decrease in complex carbohydrates.[4] Eating well involves more than passing on the chips or twinkies.

Nearly all research on PMS indicates that poor diet is related to a higher incidence of symptoms. Caffeine, sugar, salt, and fat combined with low levels of certain vitamins and minerals in our diets can greatly increase PMS symptoms of depression, irritability, anxiety, and water retention, as well as more painful periods. The kind of things which often create the greatest problem are the ones we crave the most if we are out of tune with our bodies and out of balance in a holistic sense. We need to feed our bodies what they need all the time but particularly around our Moontime.

So what do our bodies really want? Most research on nutrition and PMS suggests a natural foods diet. This means reducing drastically the processed foods you consume. Using whole grains and beans, fresh fruit and vegetables (organically grown if you can get them), reducing meat consumption (particularly beef and chicken which has been factory farmed), using dairy products in moderation, and drastically decreasing or eliminating sugar, caffeine, alcohol. Decreasing simple sugars and increasing complex carbohydrates (grains and veggies) alone alleviates symptoms of PMS. The problem with eating the average American diet is that we become deficient in the vitamins and minerals which are intricately involved in regulation of hormones. For example, deficiency in B vitamins has been found in women who suffer from PMS. Because B vitamin deficiency creates a high level of estrogen and high estrogen depletes B vitamins, we have a vicious circle. Women who are on birth control pills are further depleted of B vitamins and other vitamins and minerals (for example, one half of all Pill users are below the normal range for B12).[5] The high level of estrogen this creates not only accentuates PMS symptoms but is linked to cancer of the breast and uterus. While supplemental vitamins and minerals have been used with success in reducing PMS symptoms, eating a natural diet rather than a processed one is ideal.

The vitamins and minerals which have been shown to be therapeutic for PMS are vitamin B6, C, E, magnesium, and calcium.

Vitamin B6 has been demonstrated in a number of studies to control premenstrual tension and depression. It also seems to be linked to dream recall. B6 deficiency is associated with poor or no dream recall. Particularly rich sources of B6 are nutritional yeast, pecans, potatoes, salmon, raw vegetables, and whole grains. Vitamin C has been used to alleviate back pain associated with monthly cramps and it aids in the absorption of iron. Vitamin E relieves pain of menstrual cramps and decreases breast tenderness. It is naturally found in the oils of grains, nuts, seeds, corn, soybean and safflower. For menstrual cramps 30 to 200 IU per day of vitamin E has been therapeutic.[6]

Magnesium deficiency is associated with muscle spasms, twitching, irregular heart beat, insomnia, anxiety, and depression. The level of magnesium is naturally lowest during menstruation and has been found to be especially low in women with PMS. Diuretics can accentuate PMS by increasing the excretion of both potassium and magnesium. Some natural sources of magnesium are kelp, brewer's yeast, alfalfa sprouts, beet root tops, dried fruits, sunflower and pumpkin seeds, raw nuts, raw or lightly steamed leafy green vegetables, beans, corn, brown rice, wheat germ and oatmeal. Some natural diuretics which do not cause magnesium excretion are cranberry juice, kelp, parsley, and watercress.

Calcium levels in the body drop about 10 days prior to menstruation and remain low until the end of the cycle.[7] Symptoms of low calcium are swelling, weight increases, headaches and other PMS symptoms. Increasing calcium in the diet decreases tension, irritability, and menstrual cramps. Eating too much red meat or drinking soda pop, both of which have high phosphorus levels disrupts the normal phosphorus/calcium ratio in the body and produces symptoms of low calcium. The two minerals which American women are most deficient in are calcium and iron. Our high meat and soda pop consumption contributes to the problem.

Your car would not do very well if you decided to start feeding it a little sugar along with its gas. Our bodies are far more intricately balanced than the engine in your car, yet we feed it all sorts of unnatural things and expect it to perform well and not clog up.

That is not a very rational expectation. While most people would agree with this, eating well is not very easy in today's world. We have become dependent on fast, processed foods in our fast paced lives. It takes time to prepare meals from whole foods which, for the most part, can't be just moved from the freezer to the microwave to your plate in five minutes or less. While there are a greater variety of microwavable, organic, frozen products available, they are often expensive and not found in the average grocery store.

A good way to begin working on good eating habits is to assess how you are eating now. Get a small notebook and begin recording everything that goes into your mouth. After a week you should be able to see what needs modifying and where you can begin changing your diet. It is also important to become aware of the labels on the food you are eating. The ingredients are listed in order of the percentage of the product, so if sugar is listed first, there is more of it than anything else in the product.

Everyone's body is slightly different, so it is important to listen to your own body's needs. Cravings, as long as they are not for addictive substances, often indicate a need which you should honor. I recall one time I had a craving for lima beans and would eat a whole package at a time. It turned out that I had a potassium deficiency and that lima beans are one of the highest foods in potassium. Once you start to eat better, you will find that you can trust your body more to tell you what it needs. There is an excellent book called *Pro-Vita Plan* which gives a lot of good information on how to eat for maximal health and vitality.[8]

Herbs

People have used plants since the beginning of time, successfully treating many different kinds of problems and diseases. It is often thought that many of the packaged and processed medicines we have today came from plants and that they are a simple way to get the active ingredient from the plant. However, treatments using herbs, plants and other natural remedies require a holistic relationship between the plant, the medicine person, and the patient. When Europeans first came to North America and observed native medicine people using plants for healing, they asked where they learned which plant could be used for what. The native people said that the plants told them.

Today in many schools of herbalism, learning to tune into the plant is an important part of the training. It reflects the understanding that one cannot separate the "active ingredient" from the plant and retain the same effect. Often the other qualities of the plant buffer or enhance the medicinal qualities of that ingredient. The spirit of the plant also plays a roll in the effectiveness of the treatment. This seems rather "far out" from the point of view of Western medicine, but is well known among the medicine people and shamans from whom Western scientists seek the "active ingredients" that cure illness. In medieval Europe much of the knowledge of herbs was stamped out as patriarchy took over healing, and women's healing practices were made illegal and suppressed. It is no wonder that the European men who came to the Americas thought the natives were trying to fool them.

There are several good sources of information on herbs which are helpful for women's health. Rosemary Gladstar Slick has a book called *Herbal Healing for Women* in which she gives many different herbal formulas for treating a variety of women's health issues.[9] She discusses the herbal treatment of pain and cramps, excessive bleeding, lack of menstruation, premenstrual syndrome, and yeast infection and gives general tonic teas to strengthen the reproductive system as well. As with all herbal treatment it is seen within the overall context of nutrition and as a process strengthening your body to remove the problem rather than a quick fix which masks the problem. Other books are *Hygia: A Women's Herbal* by Jeannine Parvati[10] and *Wise Women's Herbal for the Childbearing Year* by Susun Weed.[11]

One herbal tea from Rosemary Gladstar Slick's book is used as a female tonic to nourish the reproductive system and endocrine glands. It includes: 2 parts Raspberry leaf, 1 part Strawberry leaf, 1 part Comfrey leaf, 2 parts Nettle, 2 parts Peppermint and/or Spearmint, 2 parts Lemon Grass, and 1/2 part Squaw Vine.[12] These herbs can be obtained from an herb store or from your own garden if you are familiar with these plants. Pour boiling water over one teaspoon of the dried herbs per cup of water, steep for 10 minutes, and strain. She suggests drinking the tea daily. If you make a batch, it can be stored in the refrigerator in a glass jar for several days.

Another herb which has gained some attention in the treatment of PMS is Evening Primrose. Stella Weller reviews the research on the use of this herb, finding very positive effects.[13] A dosage of two 500 mg capsules of Efamol (Evening Primrose oil) twice a day after food from about three days before the symptoms were anticipated until menstruation began was effective. The vitamin mineral compound Efavit (vitamin C, niacin, pyridoxine, and zinc) was used in some cases to enhance the effect of the Evening Primrose oil. In most studies, nearly 70% of women treated gained total relief from such PMS symptoms as breast pain, depression, irritability, anxiety, headaches and fluid retention. In other studies it was used to treat menstrual irregularities and prolonged bleeding with similar success.

There are also PMS teas and Female Reproductive System Toner teas on the market already made up in tea bags. Traditional Medicinal Tea Company has several teas for women as well as many other tea treatments. Some grocery store and most health food or natural food stores stock them. Using herbs is another way in which we can bring our bodies into rhythm with the natural cycles of nature and enhance our connections to the Earth. Recognizing the intricate beauty in the flowers and herbs gives us a reflection of our own beauty.

Exercise

Regular exercise helps us to be more beautiful in many ways. Not only does it tone muscles of the body including your most important belly, it tones the inner workings of your nervous system and digestive system as well. It releases brain chemicals which help you to feel good. There are many different ways to exercise so you should try to find one you enjoy, because then you will be more likely to do it. I like variety, so I give myself a choice of ways in which I can exercise, but I don't give myself the choice of not exercising. Walking is a great exercise both for its effect on your body and because it gets you outdoors. Another very beneficial exercise is yoga. After you learn some of the stretches either through a class or a book, it can be practiced in 15 to 20 minutes a day at home. There are a variety of yoga positions which are good for menstrual cramps and general strengthening of the pelvic area. The butterfly, pelvic tilt, plow, star, spinal twist, pelvic stretch, pelvic thrust, child pose, and shoulder stand are all good stretches (although inverted postures should not be done during actual bleeding).[14] Most yoga books or classes teach these. Another stretch used by women since the beginning of time is the squat. Before chairs this was a common position for resting. It is also the most natural position for elimination or child birth. It is interesting how such a natural and relaxing position for our ancestors is so difficult for us now. The position is one where your feet are flat on the floor (not on your toes) and fairly wide apart. You then squat down leaning far enough forward to keep your balance. Most women today find this quite difficult at first, but with practice, it becomes much easier. You can try to incorporate this position into your everyday life by squatting to weed the garden, clean something off the floor, or just to rest while outside. The good part is that you don't need anything to sit on. The squat, also referred to as the frog position, alleviates menstrual cramps. It works well.

The most important thing to remember about exercise is to do it. We get very little exercise in our daily work compared to women 50 years ago so we need to devote at least a small portion of our day to taking care of our bodies in this way. It creates beauty on the inside and outside.

Rest

It would seem obvious that our bodies need sleep and rest, but too often we place more importance on what we have to get done. Rest means sleep but it also means time out to do nothing or anything. I once heard that the ideal way of living is to work for eight hours, sleep for eight hours, and play for eight hours each day. As women we tend to come up short on both the play and sleep end. Sleeping is your body's time to rebuild itself, regain energy, and reorganize information. We have already seen that while your body is resting other parts of you are quite active in your ongoing inner life of dreams. Research has shown that the most significant part of our sleep time for our psychological well-being is the time we spend dreaming. When deprived of dreaming we become irritable, depressed, and our performance on a variety of tasks drops. Another interesting finding is that just prior to and during Moontime we seem to have a greater need to sleep. One researcher reported that just by allowing women to sleep more at that time many symptoms of PMS were reduced.

There are other times in our cycle when we need less sleep. Many women feel more energized and feel less like sleeping both when they ovulate and on the full Moon (which naturally would occur together). It is important to know your own sleeping needs. For some women eight hours is fine, others need nine and some find six is adequate.

Another interesting sleep pattern which I hear from women is that they find themselves awake in the middle of the night. This appears to be a very creative time for some people and if you find this happening regularly, you might want to make use of it by writing, or doing other creative work rather than fretting about it. Again, tuning into your own body's rhythms is important for coming into and remain in a balanced state.

Body care

Taking care of your body also means doing the things which help your body to feel good all over. There are many possibilities here all of which require you to treat yourself to something nice. A hot bath is always a good treat, especially if you include some sweet smelling bath salts or essential flower oils. I find a bath with sea salt in it very cleansing, or you can rub the salt on your body while taking a shower. Lighting incense or a fragrant candle while you soak in the tub is also nice. Then, of course, there is full body massage or other types of body work. If you don't have the money for a massage, get your partner or a friend, a book on massage, and learn to massage each other.

Treat yourself to dancing. Put on your favorite music and dance your feelings. Women are always saying how much they love to dance but rarely do. Dancing brings our feet into the rhythms of the Earth and the vibrations of beauty around us as it integrates the parts of ourselves into wholeness.

Taking care of our bodies in all these ways, eating right, using herbs, exercising regularly, resting, and treating ourselves provides a strong foundation from which our beauty can grow.

Beauty on an Emotional Level

Our emotions are cyclical and will be ever changing like the tides. We can become more beautiful as we learn to use our emotions as learning experiences and develop a sense of inner peace with the process. Anger, fear and sadness will always be with us, but they can become our friends rather than enemies. They teach us and motivate us to change. We can begin to trust the process by knowing that there really are important lessons to be learned and that we are being guided through the process if we only take the time to listen. So beauty on an emotional level is not being unemotional or unchanging, but staying in your center as you experience all emotions. In your center there is no blame of yourself or others and no guilt, only learning.

When you can stay more and more in your center the resulting peacefulness allows you to move through your life centered in love. Moving from a loving center means that you can accept and love yourself and others as they are, beautiful spirits on an Earth walk. While this might sound rather idealistic, it is what the growth process is leading you toward. As you begin to see yourself as all you are, you can view others as all they are. Love for both yourself and others is easy to find from this perspective. It is finding and keeping that perspective that is difficult to do while we experience our lessons. There is a beautiful story from a novel written by Patricia Nell Warren called One is the Sun. One young Native American woman is telling the story to a young German woman as a way of explaining the Medicine Wheel. I include it here to help you remember.

"When I was getting ready to be born," said River Singing, looking out at the lightning-lit horizon with shining eyes, "I found that I was in the most amazing place! It was the center of a sparkling Circle.

"This Circle sometimes looked like lightning running all around the horizon! Sometimes it looked like a river of northern lights, or a necklace of a thousand Moons dancing. At other times, it looked like ten billion shining fish swimming round and round me.

"When I began to look more closely, I saw that there were four principal places on the Circle. But they were empty.

"Somehow I knew that something, or someone, needed to be in those four places! The Circle was not complete!

"And so I willed to see what ought to be there!

"The moment that I wished, four young Goddesses appeared in those places!

"I didn't know they were Goddesses, because I was just a tiny baby, the size of a minnow, and incredibly ignorant. But I knew that they were very special, somehow—very powerful and magical.

"Each held a shining object in Her hands. I couldn't see what the things were, and I was very curious! So I tried to lean out and

look more closely—in all four directions at once! You can imagine how I stretched myself!"

As River Singing imitated how she would stretch her long neck
to the four directions, Sun Maiden giggled. After they both had a
good laugh, River Singing continued her story:

"'We are here to present you with your Gifts,' the young
women said to me. Their voices were like four creeks running
gently together in a great meadow.

"'My Gifts?' I repeated. 'Don't I already have everything that I
need to be born? Fingers? Toes? Nose? Bellybutton?'

"'These,' they said, 'are the Gifts that every child is given by
Mother Earth, so that the child can experience Life. No child is
ever forgotten. Every child is given these Gifts in a different way,
because each is a different person. But every child has them. And
now we, the daughters of Earth, are here to give them to you.'

"And their voices were like four gentle breezes blowing
together around the top of a great mountain.

"'I am Fire Beauty, and I give you the first Gift,' hummed the
woman in the East. She was a wondrously bright and shining
Goddess, dressed in a robe of summer sunlight. She was holding
out to me a glowing little golden sphere. Behind Her was the
blackest and deepest of night skies, all speckled with stars.

"'Here,' She said, 'is the Gift of your own spirit. Spirit is pure
light and energy. It is how the Sun lives. It is your power to
illuminate yourself with your own experience. In this way, you can
be enlightened by Life. You can see spirit with the eyes of spirit.'

"Her voice had a wondrous sound. It sounded a little like the
buzzing of a hummingbird.

"And She placed the Gift not into my hand... but right into my
being.

"As I was inspecting the wonderful new Gift, I heard a second
voice. This one sounded like a soft whisper in a deep cave, far
beneath the Earth, where crystals grow.

"'Sweet one, I am Earth-Beauty, the Goddess of the West,' said
the voice.

"The second Goddess was incredibly dark. Not dark like some
dark skinned humans, but really black—like a winter night. She
was so black that I could begin to see colors in Her, like when we
are in the Rainbow Lodge. Her robe was iridescent with the
deepest hues of blue and purple. Behind Her was a sky that shone
like a dome of yellow iron.

"Into my being, She placed a sphere of blue light.

"'I give you your body,' She said. 'This is the substance of Mother Earth, that your spirit is being born into. Only in substance can you look-within—to see into your own being. In this way, you can experience your powers of introspection and intuition.'

"And she placed the blue sphere into my being. I could actually see it, glowing within me!

"By now, I was beginning to feel incredibly rich, and so I turned to the South, knowing that a Gift must be there also.

"In the South place on my Circle, there was a graceful Goddess whose body appeared to be made of the richest russet leaves, crimson vines, and delicate red-brown bark. Her robe was the most delicate red-pink haze of autumn rosebuds. Behind Her was a white sky—clouds blowing swiftly in the wind.

"'My Gift,' She said in a voice like a tremolo through a hollow reed, 'is emotion. I am Water-Beauty.'

"She held it out to me—and it looked like..."

River singing paused, dreaming for a moment, imagining. She was creating the story as she went along. Then she said:

"It looked like a glowing rose, with drops of dew shimmering all around it.

"'This,' She said, 'is your great river of feelings. It will carry you like the mighty waters into your power to trust —your power to be truly innocent, meaning your power to know when you truly know a thing.'

"And she placed it into my being.

"Finally the Goddess of the North stepped toward me.

"'My Gift,' She said, 'is called the mind. I am Wind-Beauty. You cannot experience it unless you experience the first three Gifts as well. Through your mind, you can know what you see around you, what you see within you, what you feel. In this way, you will touch knowledge and wisdom.'

"Her voice sounded like the beating of the wings of ten thousand tiny white butterflies.

"As She spoke, her cloud-robes seemed to sheen and change, churning into cumulus clouds, clearing into high clean cirrus clouds that shimmered with every delicate pearly color of a spring day. Behind Her was a crimson sunset reflected into a still lake.

"When She had placed her Gift into my being, all of the Goddesses spoke together again, and their voices sounded like..."

River Singing stopped to imagine again. "They sounded like something that I haven't heard yet—something wonderful that I know exists. And they said:

"'If you care for all four of these Gifts, they will grow in power, and you will experience the greatest Gift of all!'

"'What is that?' I asked them.

"'It is the Gift of choice—of becoming a true human Self. Only the Self of the human can truly experience spirit, body, emotion and mind in balance with one another! But no one can give you this Gift! Not even our Mother Earth!'

"This frightened me. A Gift that I had to have ... but that no one could give me, not even Mother Earth?

"'Then how will I find it?' I cried.

"'You can choose to become a Self,' they said. 'The choice itself, and the becoming, is the Gift.'

"'You...' said the East.

"'...must...' said the West.

"'...give it...' said the South.

"'...to...' said the North.

"'... yourself,' they said all together.

"As they said these words, I was born."

River Singing paused for a long time. Then she added, with a laughing rush:

"And I instantly forgot everything that the beautiful Goddesses told me! And now I am fighting to remember what they said, and who I am!"

Helle sat glowing with the magic that the story had created around the two of them.

"Earth Thunder told me once," River Singing went on, "that most people never experience being a real Self in their whole lives. They never sit in the center of their Circle, and learn about all their powers, and direct them equally. They wander lost on the edge of the Circle, and their powers run wild like untrained horses."[15]

The lessons we are continually learning help us to remember who we really are and to stand at the center of our Circle.

Another aspect of emotional beauty is using our emotion to motivate us toward action. In a positive way, we can see this driving force as a fire which lives within our bellies. The fire may only be small coals which need to be fanned by our conscious breath, but it is there. When this fire burns we are filled with passion for life. Things which you are passionate about are often in the areas where you have gifts to give. The fire will also burn away those things you no longer need, cleaning out the excess baggage. It feeds and energizes our creativity.

So how do you light this fire? Many of us have been taught that a man will create this fire, this passion within us. However, when we let someone else be our fire keeper, we are at their mercy when it comes to feeling passionate about life and having control over our own creative force. Learn to tend your own fire. Begin by breathing and visualizing the coals being fanned and small flames bursting forth. Check on your fire daily and breath more life into it. Ask that it cleanse you of things you no longer need. Pay attention to those things which create passion in you and see where they lead you.

There are many activities which also provide fuel for the fire. Dancing is one already mentioned. It allows you to move from your belly and the creative force, really grounding you in your body and getting you out of your head. Singing is another way to fuel the fire. Sing songs everyday that are meaningful to you. There are many songs coming forth now which reach the fire within us and caress the flames, drawing them upward. Doing craft work or any creative work also provides fuel for the fire of passion. Fires which are not regularly tended burn down and need to be re-kindled again. If you regularly feed your fire it will provide energy and motivation for your life's work.

Beauty on a Spiritual Level

The primary way we create beauty on a spiritual level is by speaking our truth. When I say this to women it often brings the response of "But I'm not even sure what my truth is." Certainly doing inner work helps us to recognize the truth, but I believe that all women already know many truths and because they have been told they are wrong, they doubt themselves. All women know deep down that no one should be beaten, they know by how they feel when they see it happen. But they allow it to happen, to themselves and to others. They do not speak their truth.

If you really want to get in touch with your truth, write down what bothers you just prior to and during your Moontime. Women have been taught to be silent and to doubt their inner voice. It is now time to speak. Speaking the truth also cuts through the games, all the dysfunctional family games and political games that are being played today. Speaking the truth is like the boy in the story of the Emperor's New Clothes. The king wore no clothes but everyone in the kingdom pretended he did so as not to offend him. The young boy called the game when he spoke the truth about what was happening: the king was naked!

Speaking the truth is a lot like being that boy. You often feel like the only one who sees the truth (which of course makes you doubt yourself even more) and even after you speak it everyone else denies it. Much of this is present in cases of sexual abuse. When the one who has been abused finds the courage to speak, the abuser denies it. It takes a lot of courage to speak and there is much fear in doing so. Assertiveness techniques might help her overcome the fear and give her words to say what must be said in the most effective way possible. I have found that, for women, if the assertive statement is preceded by a preparatory statement and followed by a caring statement, it is often more effective. An example would be, "I have something important to say to you. I feel very angry when you come home in a bad mood and take it out on me. We need to do something different here or I will be leaving the house each time it happens. I am telling you this because I care about you and our relationship." The important elements in this example were: (1) a preparatory statement; (2) an assertive statement which used "I" language focusing on how you feel plus an action to be taken if things don't change; (3) a caring statement. The action statement isn't needed the first time something is brought up, but if change has been promised and has not occurred or your feelings have been ignored, the action statement is necessary. Never say that you will do something which you cannot actually do, since in most cases you may end up doing it at least once. I call this the PIC method because it involves Preparation, I statements and Caring statements. Regardless of how we do it, each of us must speak our truth whether it is heard not. We must speak because it is our truth and we must speak to weave our truth with that of other women. Through this weaving of the truth, we will have a beautiful web which supports us all.

Another aspect of beauty from a spiritual level is walking your truth. That's right, it's not enough to speak it, you have to walk it too! The saying, walk your talk, or walk your truth, means that you must live the things you believe in. If you care about the Earth, you recycle. If you believe that there is spirit in all things, then you thank the spirit in the food you are eating for giving its life to you. If you see world peace as a goal, then you create it within your own heart. Walking your truth is very difficult but something we need to strive for. Again it is not about being perfect, but working toward a goal.

The other way in which we achieve beauty on a spiritual level is by being in good relationship with all things. Every religious tradition has in its legends a person who came to Earth to remind humans about being in good relationship. Whether it was Jesus, Mohammed, Buddha, the Dawn Star, Deganowida, or White Buffalo Calf Pipe Woman, the message was the same. Good relationship means treating other people as if they are our brothers and sisters. It means that the plants, trees, animals, and rocks are our brothers and sisters too. It means that the Earth is the mother of us all and the rivers her blood. If we disconnect from the larger Circle of life and see ourselves as separate, then we are diseased, just as we would be if we took care of our minds but not our bodies. Being whole in a spiritual sense means understanding this connection to all things and being in good relationship with everyone and everything else in the Circle. Again this is difficult. We are just beginning to develop our awareness about how intricate this relationship is. But on a practical level, it means being aware and respectful of what is around you. Taking the life of a plant or animal for food can be done with respect for that life form as a relative. Be aware of the ground you walk on and whose habitat was destroyed to build your house or to provide you with fire wood. Awareness and respect are the most important parts of being in good relationship. We can change our ways where possible, but where we cannot, at least we can be respectful.

As you can see, all of these levels influence each other and are all interrelated. It is important to work on our physical, emotional, and spiritual beauty together. The beauty which is achieved is more than skin deep, it is beauty that does not fade with age but grows, and it can be seen by everyone. Most important, you will feel truly beautiful as you embrace this process of becoming.

8

Claiming Our Beauty and Power

Gifts and Lessons

Dawn carefully picked the mint leaves and chamomile flowers from the herb garden. She remembered to ask the plant's permission and to say thank you. It seemed like the herbs were smiling and seemed happy to see her.

"Here, Grandmother, there are enough for a pot of tea."

"That looks just right," said Grandmother as she poured the boiling water over the fresh flowers and leaves in the tea pot. When the tea was ready they each took a cup and went out to sit on the porch swing.

"You know, Grandmother, you have been teaching me so many things, I feel like I don't know where to start. There are so many things I feel I should be doing differently, I even have a hard time remembering them all."

"What we have been talking about are things that are important to know for your journey through womanhood. That journey is not made in one step all at once. There are many steps you will take that will move you along this path. Maybe we can simplify it by dividing your work into two parts. One part is what we could call assuming your power as a woman. This doesn't mean assuming power over anything or anyone outside yourself. Instead it means getting in touch with your power within, that power which allows you to be who you really are and live in harmony with the whole Circle of life around you. Changes that we make in ourselves which allow us to assume more of this power could be called acts of power.

"We also have gifts to give. Each of us has our own unique talents, our own songs, which are important to the harmony of the universe. So we also must find and develop those gifts and give them away. Only through giving can we receive and, thus, complete the cycle of connection that exists within the whole Circle of life. We can refer to the process of giving our gifts away as acts of beauty.

"So if we look at our growth process at any point in time we have only two things on which to focus—an act of power or an act of beauty."

"So what your are saying is that I should pick one thing to work on to help me get in touch with my inner power and one area where I have some gift to give and find a way to give it. But I'm not sure I really have any gifts developed enough to give away yet."

"One gift we all have is the gift of ourselves. Taking the time to just be with someone who needs the company is a gift. Even a small child can learn to give of themselves. Smiling at people you see each day is a gift. An act of beauty might be to smile at each person you see every day."

"Well, that doesn't sound too hard. I guess remembering to do it would be the hard part."

"An act of power might be to remember to write your dreams down in a dream journal, to take 15 minutes a day to meditate, or to say thank you to the plants and animals for nourishing you each time you eat. If you focus on only one act of power and one act of beauty at a time, this process of learning becomes much more

130

manageable. When you have accomplished these, then you can move on to other acts of power and beauty."

"That certainly makes the process a lot clearer. I'm really excited to sit down and decide what I want to work on first."

"Another thing that is helpful is to write down what the acts of power and beauty are that you are currently working on. You can put symbols for them somewhere so you will see them each morning and evening. You can also share what you are working on with a friend or a group of friends who are engaged in the same process. It also helps to have a timeline in mind so you don't end up procrastinating on getting started or put it last on your list of things to do. These things we work on often stretch us in some way and are, therefore, uncomfortable. So any support or structure that can be created for helping us work on our acts of power and beauty is useful."

"That sounds exciting. I think I'll get Rose to work with me on my power and beauty acts. I think that the first act of power I will work on will be to meditate for 15 minutes every morning. I do it now sometimes but I give myself lots of excuses for not doing it, like I'm too tired or too busy. I think for my act of beauty, I will offer my time to a mother who needs help with something for 6 hours each week. Does that seem like an act of beauty?"

"That seems like a very good act of beauty. Mothers never have enough hands or time to do all that needs to be done and your help will be a true gift to them. After you have accomplished meditating 15 minutes each day for a couple of months and made it a firm habit, you will be ready to add another act of power."

"I can't wait to tell Rose about this. I'm going to find her now. Thanks for the tea Grandmother and thanks for the teaching too!"

"You are more than welcome, my daughter. May you use them both well. But before you run off I want to give you a song about making your dreams and visions real in the world. This song has been sung by many women as they have walked their beauty into the physical world by completing their acts of power and beauty.

"I walk a Path of Beauty, walk a path my ancestors laid
   down before me
I walk a Path of Beauty, walk a path my ancestors laid
   down before me
I make a Path of Beauty, hold my visions, roll my dreaming out before me
I make a Path of Beauty, hold my visions, roll my dreaming out before me."[1]

Where to Begin

When we think about all the things we would like to change and
work on in ourselves, sometimes it is overwhelming. It is helpful to
understand that change is a slow process, and even though we
know that we would like to end up at a certain place, we are not
aware of the sequence or number of steps it takes to get there
from here. Living in our push button society often leads us to look
for an easier way or to get discouraged when the work is difficult
and we don't seem to be making a lot of progress. There is a
certain discipline required of us by this process of change and, at
the same time, there are rhythms of working hard interspersed
with dormancy. At any rate there is no getting around the fact that
it is hard work and it takes longer than you think it should.

There are steps in the change process which are fairly similar
regardless of the type of change. The first step is awareness. We
need to be aware both of what we need to change and how it
needs to be changed. This awareness is often brought about by
emotional reactions to situations where change is necessary. The
emotion builds to the point that we either pay attention to what
needs to change or suffer the consequences of physical or emotional dis-ease. Sometimes denial is so strong it actually takes a
disease to capture our attention.

132

Once we are aware that something needs to change we need to plan some course of action which will create that change. Much of this work is a combination of head work and inner work. Where is your path leading you? What do you need to let go of? How can you view things differently? Once you understand what needs to change and have some idea of what you need to do differently to bring about that change, the next step is to begin the process. This is often where fear comes in. Mostly it is fear of the unknown, but it often also includes a fear of how others may react.

At this point you may remain stuck for a while, paralyzed by the fear or not wanting to face the issue until things get so uncomfortable and the voice inside is so demanding that you are ready to jump off the cliff and try your new wings. Your first attempts at flying will be neither as bad nor as good as you imagined. The best laid plans for change always need fine tuning. Once you have arrived at the point of beginning to put the change plan into action, you will need to do a lot of analysis after situations occur to move to the place you wish to be with the new behavior. This is true for any new behavior or habit. If you were learning to play tennis, you would first get the idea of what needed to happen (racket contacting ball and directing it with a certain force in a certain direction), and then you would try it and modify the next swing according to the results of the first swing. It is important to be easy on ourselves at this point. Knowing in your head what needs to be done does not translate into being able to do it perfectly. Give yourself pats on the back for the good attempts you make and then see how you can improve the next time.

Another thing I feel that I should mention here, is that you are not in competition with anyone else to see who can change the most or the fastest. Your journey is yours alone. We are all on different journeys. Even though it may appear that two people are working on the same thing, the lessons involved are often different in many ways. There are no comparisons to be made, just acknowledgement that the general process in which we are all involved is the same. We need to support others in their change process regardless of how slow or fast it is moving. We can do that because we have all been in both the slow and fast lanes ourselves. I also feel that each of us is guided and our inner guide knows far more about the journey than anyone else could possibly know. Trusting in the process allows us to accept ourselves and others wherever we are in the process.

Once we feel comfortable with the change we have made, we still need to maintain it. Humans have a wonderful ability to slip back to old habits when attention is lost. So having a way to maintain and build on the change as an ongoing process helps to keep from slipping back. Then we are ready for a new change to take place and we repeat the cycle.

Acting in a Powerful Way

There has been a great misunderstanding about power. "Power over" people and things has been the way in which our society and many others have viewed power. "Power within" is something which we are just beginning to understand in Western societies. Perhaps because women have experienced less "power over" in recent history (except, of course, being the ones who the power was over), they are more open to understanding "power within."

On the desk in my office I have a sign which reads "A woman's place is in control." Women look at the sign and nod their heads making a remark about how they need to be more in control of themselves. Men read the sign and become angry interpreting it to mean that a woman's place is in control of them. I'm not sure what the reactions would be if the sign referred to men being in control, but it does seem to be a generality that, in our society, women more often seek to control themselves and men more often seek to control others.

What is power within? It is the power which comes from knowing yourself, speaking your truth, walking your talk, all of the things which we have talked about so far. It is an inner knowing that needs no outer validation. It is a passion for living your life fully and with integrity. When we do things which increase our inner

134

power, we are simply doing things which allow us to live more consistently and more authentically with our true selves. This powerful way of living centers us and aligns us with the power of the universe. As you begin to move more toward your center, things begin to fall in place for you in the outer world. I have experienced this myself and have seen it happen to others. The lessons we encounter tend to throw us off center again, and as we learn more of the lesson we return to center. Claiming your power is about the learning of lessons and making the journey to your center.

The process of claiming power can be conceived of as commitment to doing things which bring you closer to your center. It is commitment to an action, made in response to a lesson, which brings about change. These acts of power are always things which are difficult to do and sometimes things which you would rather not do or would procrastinate over. It requires courage to face our fear, the fear of looking at ourselves and the fear of change. What is an act of power for one person may not be for another. What you do well already may be my challenge and what I do well is yours. So in that sense, it is an act performed alone. An example of an act of power for me was to devote 15 minutes each morning to meditation. Morning is a time when I want to be running off in all directions doing lots of things. I have learned from experience that I am more productive if I take the time to get centered before I start my day. It was initially very hard for me to just sit for 15 minutes when my mind was telling me about lots of other "more important" things I "should" be doing. Making a commitment to meditate each morning created inner power.

There are many actions which create power. Basically, it is committing yourself to any action which furthers you along your path and brings you closer to center. It may be any of the things which have been talked about in previous chapters: keeping a dream journal, eating better, meditating, exercising, taking time for yourself at Moontime, doing inner work, journaling. It could also be things like dealing with a relationship which is unworkable, refusing to play the usual family games, changing jobs, learning new skills, finding a support group, or changing your usual reaction to a situation. You know the things your inner voice has been nagging you to do and on which you have been procrastinating. The important thing is to formulate your act of power in very concrete terms and even give yourself a deadline. When doing so, both the action and the deadline should be realistic. If I want to meditate 15 minutes each morning as a goal, I might start out by saying that I will meditate 10 minutes five days per week for the next month and then move to 15 minutes six days a week the second month and finally be up to 15 minutes seven days a week by the third month. If I needed to speak to a friend about our relationship, I would write down what I needed to say and give myself a deadline of four weeks to say it.

The reason these actions need to be specific and with deadlines is to provide clarity and motivation for carrying through and actually performing them. The clearer you are about what needs to be done, the more likely you are to do it. If you have a deadline, then you are less likely to procrastinate by waiting for "the right time" to do something. It also allows you time to get your courage together.

The last thing to keep in mind about these acts of power is that they should push you beyond where you are now. Doing something which might sound powerful to someone else but is easy for you is not an act of power. If it does not require courage or discipline and is not difficult for you to do, it is not an act of power. Some things which sound very easy are the most difficult to do. I recall one woman committing to being conscious of the plants and animals which gave their lives each meal she ate and thanking them. I thought to myself at the time, "Is that all she is going to do?" Later I had the opportunity to try the same thing myself and found it most difficult. An act of power must be hard to do, but not impossible.

The Give Away

While acts of power address our need to grow and become more centered, acts of beauty address our need to offer our own special gifts to the world. Beauty is something which is to be shared. Sometimes we are afraid to share our beauty, afraid it will not be good enough or that we need to be perfect first. We all have beautiful gifts which can be shared. Sometimes the gift is shared with people and sometimes with other beings in the Circle of Life. Caring for animals, plants, and trees is beauty shared. Knowledge of herbs, crafts, gardening, life, people, cooking, etc., can be shared in a beautiful way both through what you create and what you say. Peaceful energy is a gift in any setting. The giving helps us keep the connection with others strong. We give of our gifts, not to get back from others, but to create beauty. Gifts which are shared grow within us, feeding us. That which is given freely always returns in some way to nourish us.

Sometimes I hear women say that they are tired of giving. They have given and given of themselves and have received little in return. It is possible to give yourself away if that is all you are doing and you are not taking the time to give to yourself what you need to grow and be centered. In other words, acts of beauty without acts of power to accompany them are out of balance. Sometimes giving to others feels better than facing our own lessons, so we hide in the giving. When you are giving from a place of power within you, when you are well-nourished and moving from your own beauty, giving does not diminish you, but enhances you.

To decide on what you have to give and how you wish to give it, think of what you know how to do which will increase beauty in the world and then make it into a concrete behavior. One woman was a wonderful cook who committed to making a large pot of her delicious soup and donating it to a needy family or soup kitchen each week. Another had a group of women friends with whom she had not shared her knowledge of Moontime. She set a time and invited them over to share the information. Beauty acts can be anything: planting trees, visiting people in a nursing home, taking care of children for a burned-out mom, starting a petition to influence environmental politics in your area, getting together your neighbors to form a council for dealing with local environmental issues, child protection, etc. There is no shortage of gifts to be given or places where these gifts are needed. Creating a world of beauty begins with each of us.

Staying Motivated

Thinking up things we can do as acts of power and beauty is only part of the process. Actually doing them is the other part and probably the hardest part. I am a great one for getting up in the morning with lots of plans for what I am going to accomplish and end up reading a book, wondering where the day has gone, and feeling upset because I haven't done anything. Thus, discipline and motivation are topics I have researched and learned well. Brooke Medicine Eagle, in her book *Buffalo Woman Comes Singing*, suggests writing beauty and power action contracts as a way of motivating change.[2] The process is very similar to a behavior change contract which I have used to facilitate change in clients for everything from addictive behaviors to marital distress. As I mentioned before, acts of beauty and power must be stated very clearly with some kind of timeline. This creates motivation in and of itself. In addition, setting some kind of forfeit, something to be given up if the act is not accomplished within the timeline is helpful. While this might seem like a punishment, the purpose is to provide a strong enough consequence to motivate the action. If I were to put up as a forfeit my favorite ring which I have worn for the last 10 years or my canoe, you can be sure that I would have that act of power or beauty done by the deadline. The forfeit should be something you definitely would not want to part with. If you find yourself unwilling to put up a forfeit, then you need to ask yourself how serious you are about accomplishing the acts or if they are realistic. There are some people who always do what they commit to and don't need this extra motivation and that is just fine. You need to know yourself and tailor this process to your own needs.

Another way to build motivation is to share the process with a friend or group of friends. Your acts of power and beauty should be written down along with timelines and forfeits and copies given to your friends. You can also note how your friends can support you in this process—through phone calls, words of encouragement, or other means. You might want to write down the usual ways in which you sabotage yourself, or the excuses you usually use as to why you can't do these things. Sharing your commitments with someone else is a very powerful motivator since your excuses can no longer be private. If you have a forfeit it might be promised to someone in the group. It keeps you honest with yourself.

Your friends can also be supportive in the formulation of your acts of power and beauty, helping to clarify them and to keep them realistic. Just being a part of a group of women who are interested in growing and changing is a good source of motivation. It helps you to feel not as alone in the process. While we each have to walk our paths alone and we each might be working on different lessons, it gives me tremendous courage to know that there are others walking with me. Together we have more strength than when we are isolated.

Staying on the Path

It seems best in most cases to work on just one or possibly two acts of power and beauty at a time. If you have too many going at once, it can get overwhelming and that brings everything to a standstill. Once you have completed one act of power and beauty you can move on to another. If I have gotten to the point of meditating 15 minutes each morning and it is now a part of my routine, I might continue to do that but add writing in a dream journal or 20 minutes of yoga. I know I always want to have everything changed and accomplished all at once, but that is not very realistic. Taking things one step at a time in the change process is most productive.

Over time, one of the best things I have found to help get a sense of progress is keeping a journal, or at least making notes on what is taking place. If I can look back to six years ago and see that I had set a goal to meditate 15 minutes a day, and now see that morning meditation as an essential part of my life, I recognize that I accomplished something of great value. If we have no record of our lessons and our give aways, we often feel like we are really not doing anything and that we are moving so slowly. Any kind of record will do as long as you date it and keep it so you can look back on it from time to time to give you a feeling of motion. Many times you will find the same issue reappears a couple of years later. Without a record of your first encounter, you may have the sense that you learned nothing at all the last time. With the record you can see how your current experience is building on what you learned before. You studied math in both first and second grade. Both classes were math, but in second grade you built upon what you learned in first grade.

Seeking inner power and claiming the beauty that is ours is a process of ongoing change. Making commitments in the form of acts of power and beauty can facilitate the change process, make it more manageable and less overwhelming. Sharing the process can even make it exciting. Living happily ever after, which we all heard about as the goal of life, really means being able to grow and change and share the process with friends.

9

Rites of the Moon Women

Moon Circle

They walked through a part of the forest that Dawn had never been to before.

"Why haven't I ever been to this beautiful part of the woods before? I should think I would have found a place such as this," said Dawn as she marveled at the beautiful trees, the flowers, and the birds.

"It simply wasn't the right time yet," said Grandmother.

That certainly didn't make the reason any clearer to Dawn but she forgot the question as they came around the bend in the path to a circular clearing in the woods. There was a bubbling brook which went over a series of waterfalls, forming deep pools beneath them. The grass was green and soft and flowers were everywhere.

"Oh, Grandmother. This is an incredible place. I've never seen anything so beautiful in my whole life."

Grandmother motioned for her to sit down in the grass with her and began to speak. "This is a Moon Circle. It is where women can come for retreat when they are in Moontime. There are rules for its use and there are many ways in which it is used. Part of your first Moontime ceremony will take place here. After that you will use it with the other women."

"I thought the Moon Lodge was the circular building across the street from my house."

"It serves the same general purpose, but some things can only be done here. This is a protected place where a woman in her Moon can come to be alone or with other women for the purpose of surrounding herself with beauty—sitting by the falls and listening to the water's song, meditating, being with the flowers, the birds, the animals, singing, drumming, dancing, bathing in the pools. It is to help her make good use of her receptivity and power at that time."

"I can hardly wait to be able to come here on my Moon!"

"In warm weather, women gather here for ritual, celebration, talking Circles, singing, drumming, and dancing. We also construct a stone people's lodge here for purification before women's initiation rites. We will be doing that for you soon. There are two groups of women who meet here, sitting around the Circle of stones you see over there or gathered around the fire Circle . One is the Moon Lodge women, those women of all ages who are bleeding with the Moon. The other is the Grandmother Lodge women who no longer bleed on a monthly cycle, but hold their blood and power to nurture all things in the Circle of life. Just as you are being initiated into the Moon Lodge, Moon Lodge women will come to an age where they are ready to be initiated into the Grandmother Lodge. Then they will be expected to use the wisdom they have gained through many Moon cycles to guide the community."

"Wow! You certainly have a lot of wisdom, you must be the head Grandmother."

"There are no head Grandmothers, although the eldest are given great respect and can speak first. We are all interdependent. No one of us has the whole truth, but by putting our pieces of truth together we come much closer. The idea of coming to this place or going to the Moon Lodge in the community is that of a retreat from daily duties and concerns so that you may surround yourself with beauty and make the best use of your Moontime. The wisdom you gain from this process has a direct benefit to your community."

"What is the Moon Lodge in town like?"

"It also is a beautiful place. It is a round building with many sky lights to let in the natural light of the sun by day and Moon by night. The only lighting inside is candle light. In the center of the circular room there is an altar on which objects are placed which symbolize something important to the women who use the lodge. There is art work on the walls which represents aspects of the four directions and the great cycles of life. There are pillows all around for comfort and a great drum and other musical instruments available. On the altar is a dream book in which any women in the lodge may add their dreams to those of the others. Mostly the lodge is used day or night as a retreat for women in their Moon, but it is also used, particularly in colder weather, for women's ritual and ceremony."

"That is where Mother goes when she is bleeding. I knew she was taking time for herself and that what she was doing was very important."

"I'm glad to see that she modeled its importance for you."

"What about the rules you mentioned?"

"These are rules that the women in the lodge have all agreed upon. One rule is that no man may enter the lodge or this area of the woods without good reason and permission from the lodge members. Men have their own area for ceremony and both men and women respect each other's space. There are many times that men and women create ceremony together, but there are other times they need to be apart. A second rule has to do with personal responsibility for maintaining and creating beauty. Each woman is to leave the area in as beautiful a condition as she found it. Each woman will also respect the needs of the other when more than one woman is using the area at the same time. There are other rules that address the way in which the group of women operates. All decision making is by consensus, that is, everyone must agree. The older women may speak first but everyone must be heard."

"You mean even I will be asked to give my opinion?"

"You are of a new generation and have as much right to be heard as any. While we see the older women as having gained wisdom to share, the younger women have fresh viewpoints to offer. Each woman is also expected to take responsibility for her own issues. While the other women can offer her their experiences of a similar nature if she wishes, she alone can decide what is best for her and take the necessary action to change.

"So you see how important this is, both retreat time to find your own wisdom and a Circle of women to share that wisdom with. Your journey to wholeness is in some ways a solitary journey, but it is also meant to be a shared experience. It is always important to remember that when you give your nourishing and live-giving blood back to the Earth, the time you take and the wisdom you receive is not for you alone but for all your relations in the Circle of life as well. This is a good song to sing on your Moon to remind you of this:

"I give away this blood of life to all my relations
and I open my womb to the light
I give away this blood of life to all my relations
and I open my womb to the light
Give away, give away, give away, give away
I open my womb to the light."[1]

Women and Community

One of the saddest things I hear from women is that they do not feel the support of other women. They may have a good friend but

144

basically they do not seem to trust other women. Perhaps this comes from the way in which we live, in the absence of community. If women are involved with other women in groups, it is likely to be a social gathering. Women in our society are expected to raise children alone, do household chores alone, and be competitive in the world of work both with men and with each other. Women also do not feel a bonding with other women because they do not value the feminine qualities. The patriarchal system is the root of the problem, but women's struggle for equality has often separated women from other women. Pursuing equality is necessary, but we are now at a time when equal respect for feminine energy is most important. One part of the feminine which is coming to light and is being explored by feminist scholars in many fields, is interdependence.

For a long time women have been struggling to be independent. There are many psychological self help books to warn us of the dangers of psychological dependence. This is interpreted by many women to mean relying on anyone for anything is dependency and it often keeps women for asking for what they need from others. Men have no problem asking for what they need and are not seen as dependent. When women seek "independence," it seems to benefit the men who rely on these women to take care of their needs. That is, the "independent" woman still takes care of her man and tries to meet her own needs as well, freeing the man from responsibility to meet her needs in return. This creates a sense of isolation in the woman that leads her to feel sadness, depression and anxiety.

Women are interdependent. They need to support each other in their daily work, child rearing, and their growth. Being interdependent in a relationship means that you and your partner support each other in meeting your individual needs—physical, emotional and spiritual. We were not meant to live in isolation.

Some of the current interest in Native American beliefs stems from our yearning for a tribe, a community to which we belong, where we are supported in a holistic way and the whole Circle of life is honored. It is interesting that many Native American tribes highly value feminine qualities in both men and women. While church communities are helpful, they are separate from our every-day lives and often do not reflect a value for the feminine.

With the division of labor in many tribal communities, women worked together, and child care was a joint effort. Men also had many activities which they did together. While I am not suggest-ing that we return to a division of labor between the sexes, we do need to return to a community-based system where people within the community can support each other with equal value accorded to the contributions of both sexes.

The real question is how to begin this process in our lives now. We have been away from community for so long that none of us is very good at understanding how community works. There are a variety of interesting books out written by people who have ex-plored this question and lived in planned communities for some time. While none of them has hit the perfect formula, they have identified some important skills we need and some important ques-tions about living in community.

The way in which some women have chosen to fill the need for community in their lives is to form a Circle of women which is supportive of their growth process. The Circle may form around any one of a variety of activities, but a common one and a good place to start is a Moon Lodge. When a group of women come together for the purpose of honoring their Moontime, they are supporting each other in their physical, emotional, and spiritual growth. While is possible to have any number of women in such a lodge, somewhere around eight is a good number. Of course it would be ideal be to have a place where the women could go on their Moontime, but it is unlikely that such a place would be avail-able or that all the women would even live close enough to each other to make use of a central spot. More likely the group would meet at regular times or on the new and full Moon for a talking Circle , drumming, dancing, singing, ritual, meditation, creative work, sharing a meal, or celebrations. The location may vary but it is nice to have some outdoor space to connect with nature. This lodge would support each of the women in their Moontime practices and the growth which follows.

The talking Circle which is usually a part of women's groups of this type is somewhat different than just a discussion or sharing. A stick or feather is passed around the Circle and whoever has the talking stick has the floor. No one else may interrupt or comment on what she has said unless she asks for comments. Knowing she will not be interrupted allows a woman time to think and speak carefully and confidently. It also allows her to say something which may make her feel vulnerable without fear of spoken judgment. For the listeners, it helps to get away from feeling that they have to jump in and "fix it" when someone else is expressing emotion or describing a problem.

When you receive the talking stick and do not wish to speak you simply pass it on. The talking stick commands attention from others and feels very powerful to hold. Selecting a stick and decorating it symbols which have significance for your group, is a wonderful beginning activity for the women of the Moon Lodge. Using the talking stick is a good reminder that the function of the group is to support each in the growth process, not to take responsibility for each other. While it is fine and sometimes helpful to share your experience of a similar situation, it is important to remember that the responsibility for making decisions on how to deal with an issue lies within the person experiencing the difficulty. Trying to take responsibility for another person's problem takes away that person's power, while supporting them in solving their own problem enhances their power.

My experience has been that even if you start with only two or three women, the word gets around and the group will grow. There are many women hungering for this kind of support and community, but they don't know such a possibility exists. When you come into a group of women who are interested in honoring their feminine, their Moontime, the whole Circle of life, it will speed up your own growth process. There will be the usual personality conflicts and difficulties that occur when groups of people try to work together, but when these issues come up they can be viewed as lessons for those involved and, therefore, important to work out. The community will be strengthened by addressing them at the onset. The ideal is to bring the issue to the Circle with the talking stick and air all sides of the conflict. It is important to present the issue as an opportunity for learning rather than a problem to be solved. In a group which is dedicated to growth, each person will be a mirror for every other person in the group, reflecting what they most need to learn. Using the sacred time and space you have created within the Circle to do this work provides a unique opportunity for support in this process.

Of all the women I have known who have started Moon Lodges all over the country, most have found no difficulty in locating interested women. The main obstacle has been finding the time and making a commitment to be there. I have heard it said that the biggest task we have in life is to show up, to be fully present. A Moon Lodge is a commitment to be present for yourself and for the other women involved. It is a commitment to honor your feminine side with the time that it needs to grow. It makes a statement about your worth as a woman.

Women and Ritual

Our lives are filled with rituals of one sort or another, most of which have little meaning for us. If we interpret the word ritual as a repetitive action, we have many as we are creatures of habit. If we use another definition from Webster's dictionary, "an established procedure for a religious or other rite" where rite means "a formal ceremony or procedure prescribed or customary in religious or other solemn use," we are probably more familiar with rituals used in religious traditions as the definition suggests. Rituals, however, can be ceremonies or planned actions used in a solemn way for many parts of our growth process. Rituals may be rites of passage, for instance, or ceremonies to let go of a part of yourself which is no longer needed. Among Native Americans, as with many tribal people, there was no word for religion. It would best be translated as "way of life." So a ritual can be a formal ceremony which reflects our way of life.

As we have seen from our ancient history and studying tribal people all over the world, in many traditions women on their Moontime gathered together apart from the rest of the tribe. Ritual was one of the activities which marked the event. Rituals performed on the new and full Moons reflected the inner rhythm of women—quiet meditative ritual on the new Moon and more outward celebration on the full Moon. Rituals often set the pace for the life of the community, governing such things as hunting, the harvesting of herbs or the planting of crops. Other rituals centered around natural events such as sunrise and sunset, solstices and equinoxes, and harvest of the natural bounty of the Earth. Growth cycles were acknowledged with rituals—puberty rites, marriages, birth, achievements, entry into the Grandmother Lodge, and even death. The difference between these types of rituals and the ones we have in our own culture, is the holistic aspect of the older ritual, involving body, emotion, and spirit, as well as the integration of the whole of the community into the ritual. Thus, rituals were social events uniting the whole community or, perhaps bonding all the women or all the men of the group. When a child passed into adulthood it was recognized by all in the community in a ritual and she was treated differently because of it. While such an integrated approach to ritual was not characteristic of all tribal people, it is more common than not among people who lived close to the Earth.

The other powerful aspect of ritual is that the ritual serves as a symbol of a larger change taking place. If a group of people gather together to celebrate the fall equinox—singing, dancing, drumming, saying prayers, doing a harvest ritual—this event only marks or symbolizes the larger change taking place in nature. As plants and trees prepare for the winter we reflect upon the harvest of the year within our own lives, the lessons learned and acts of beauty and power completed. So the ritual, because it is symbolic, represents many levels of change. Change and accomplishment in our personal lives often go unmarked. Our society only recognizes outward change, often negatively, but positively if it represents achievement in our paid jobs or academic performance. The real work of life—learning the lessons—is not seen or judged as being important.

Ritual can be used to enhance our own growth process. It can move us into change and mark the lessons in a symbolic way. It helps us to get out of our heads and into our bodies, to actually feel the change. Brooke Medicine Eagle has a wonderful tape called *Healing Through Ritual Action* in which she describes a variety of ritual actions for addressing the problems we face in learning our lessons.[2] One powerful ritual for dealing with anger is to hold a stone and allow the anger to flow into it. The stone is then placed in water or buried to carry that energy back to the Earth for recycling. It can also be used for letting go of things (habits, people, etc.) which are holding you back from change, letting all those things you need to release flow out of you. Another releasing ritual is to write all the things you wish to let go of on a piece of paper and then burn it. These actions create feeling and feeling is the energy for change. When you create rituals, they need to be right for you. These personal rituals involve deciding what you wish to accomplish with the action, what would symbolize it for you, then setting a time to do it, and finally carrying it through.

Group rituals are similar, except that the ritual is planned and done by all involved. If your Moon Lodge wanted to plan a ritual to celebrate the spring equinox, you might begin with a talking Circle to find what symbolizes the meaning of the equinox to the women in your group. Each woman might offer to be in charge of some aspect of the ritual. You might think of things which represent newness, sprouting seeds, sap running in the trees, new leaves forming, birth, new visions for the year, or anything that represents a spring time in nature or your lives. In most group ceremonies there are several parts. The first part might be called an invocation, an invitation to all in the Circle of life to be present in the ceremony. This has been described in various traditions as casting a Circle or creating sacred space. An invocation might consist of having four different women call in the spirit or qualities of the four directions, two more to invite in Mother Earth and Father Sky, and one to call in the Creator, Great Mystery, Great Spirit, God/Goddess, or Mother/Father God, however one feels comfortable addressing this energy. This might be followed by a song about newness or the changing cycles of the year. An action of some kind might be next, for example, each woman could plant a seed which represents the vision and dreams she wishes to bring to fruition throughout the year. These could be combined with commitments for acts of power and beauty. Sing songs, read poetry, dance, meditate, or do whatever seems right to the group. When you are finished there is a final expression of gratefulness to all in the Circle of life who participated and, in ending, an opening of the Circle.

Perhaps the most important thing about either individual or group ritual is that it should be meaningful to you and it should involve some action other than thinking. Rituals performed by a community such as a Moon Lodge can be very empowering to all involved. They provide a way for us each to be supported and recognized as part of a community of caring sisters. When a group of people set a sacred Circle with clear intention, the process of change is accelerated.

Stepping into Circle

It takes courage to step in to a Circle of women and say, "Here I am, standing in my truth, ready to be fully present, body, mind, emotions, and spirit." A lot of women might truthfully say they don't know how to do that. None of us know how to be in our truth very well because we haven't had much practice. We have been taught by our culture to protect and hide our truth so that we will be less vulnerable. Sometimes we might have a good friend that we can be our true selves with, but many times we don't have even that. Often after years of hiding our true self, we no longer remember where we put it or if it even exists. It takes courage to come to a group of women and say, "I want to find my true self." It takes away your hiding places or at least vividly points out to you how you hide your truth. It takes courage to come to a Circle and say, "I trust that you will accept the real me as worthy." You aren't even sure that you accept yourself, how can you expect that they will accept you? It takes courage to learn from what is reflected to you by the other women in the group who are also struggling with the same fears.

We have a choice. We can stand alone in our lives, feeling isolated but safe and hidden, or we can courageously step into the power of a Circle of sisters and feel the connection that we long for—being a part of a group of women journeying along the path of beauty, finding their strength in themselves and in the connection they have to each other and to all that is. This sounds wonderful, but it is never that easy. The strength and connection are really there, but so are the lessons. Remember, where there is fear, there is a lesson to be learned. The opposite of fear is trust, a large and important lesson.

Being a part of a Moon Lodge or any Circle of women is new for most of us and very different from what we have experienced before. We learn as we go along how to be a supportive community for each other. We also learn how to handle diversity. Being in Circle with others who are very much like you is easy. We need to learn how to be in Circle with those who are quite different from us and honor our differences. If we are to ever think of moving toward a peaceful world which is community based, we need to find ways of using diversity as a source of strength within the Circle. I cannot tell you how to do this, because I too am only learning, but I know that even though paths can be quite different, we are all here for the same purpose—to learn. We need to find a way to honor the learning of others and enhance the community in the process.

Start with one or two other women and begin a Moon Lodge. Take that step into finding connection and interdependence which is part of the truth of all women.

Rites of Passage

Rites of passage mark the phases of our lives. In ancient tradition and mythology, the Triple Goddess represented woman as Maiden, Mother, and Crone. The young girl is the first phase of our lives followed by the childbearing years, and finally the grandmother or wise woman phase. Rites of passage marked the transitions from girl to woman and from woman to grandmother. The transitions which are more frequently celebrated in our culture are birth, marriage and death. The other transitions are rarely celebrated, although we usually celebrate achievement oriented transitions, such as school graduations.

The transition from girl to woman, as shown in the stories of Grandmother and Dawn, is an important one which requires instruction in what it means to be a woman as well as how to use Moontime in a sacred way. The actual ceremony, ideally, is a culmination of these teachings and marks the passage into womanhood with all its rights and responsibilities. Women are beginning to celebrate this passage with their daughters, even without the instruction as a beginning. There are two books which are helpful to girls and which portray a very positive and sacred view of menstruation: *Moontime for Kory* [3] and *The Clear Red Stone.* [4] Reading these with daughters prior to the celebration helps them to look forward to the event as a very positive experience. Many girls who would feel very self-conscious being involved in such a celebration anticipate and enjoy their passage into womanhood after reading these books.

A first Moontime celebration can include many meaningful rituals. The Circle of women can plan it and all take part. In all women's ceremonies it is symbolic for all the women to wear skirts. Wearing skirts represents women's connection to Earth, in that nothing separates our wombs, and the opening from which our blood flows, from the Earth.

Begin by smudging with sage and sweetgrass, or some other cleansing process. This introduces the girl to the importance of coming into the Circle for sacred purpose, leaving the everyday world behind. There are good Moontime songs to sing, some of which are included in this book and on tapes listed in the back. Other songs which are Earth honoring are also wonderful to sing together. Readings are also appropriate. If you are outside or have the space, dancing is meaningful. One dance which is done to the heart beat drum is the grandmother dance. You move to the left stepping on your left foot on the second beat of the heart beat and then moving your right foot over in-between. This dance can be used to dance your motherline or the line of women, mothers, grandmothers, great-grandmothers, stretching back over time.

Naomi Lowinsky suggests that our mothers are our future, who we will become, while our daughters are our past, who we were.[5] The reverse is also true, that our daughters represent the future and our mothers the past, creating a looping through time of the mother-daughter link—interlocking Circles rather than straight lines of relationship. The ceremony might also include the mother washing the feet of the daughter being celebrated, representing her leaving childhood behind and stepping freshly into womanhood.

The sharing of first Moontime stories by the women of the Circle creates intimacy and introduces the girls to the use of the talking stick. I have found that when this is done, it may be the first time the women of the group have ever talked about their first Moontime experience and it can be a powerful healing for the whole group.

The girl can then be painted with face paints. A traditional design is to paint the forehead red, while a design I've used is small red Moons across the forehead moving from full Moons on the outside to a new Moon directly in the center of the forehead. A nice touch is to have each of the women paint their "medicine" or symbols of how they see themselves as women on their faces before the ceremony. Then when the girls are painted they become like the other women, signifying the transition to womanhood. At this time a spiritual name can be given which represents what this young woman has to offer the world or who she will become as a woman, the work that she will do.

Another ritual which all girls like is gift giving. Each woman gives the girl a gift which symbolizes either something she needs to know about being a woman or some quality she has that will serve her well as a woman. It is nice to write the significance of the gift on a piece of paper or, if you can get coordinated enough ahead of time, in a special book which can be kept by the girl. Ending with song and prayers for this new woman's growth and strength, followed by a sharing of food and social time, is a nice conclusion to the event.

Another ritual which has been done in ceremonies I have heard about, is tying the wrists of the mother and daughter together and having them run until the mother can run no further. The rope then is cut and the daughter runs on. Dressing the girl in new clothes can also symbolize the transition. Still other women have created a stone people's lodge, or sweat lodge for their daughters to represent the cleansing away of their childhood and entrance into the ritual of womanhood. The list of possibilities are as large as your imagination, but remember the rituals you choose should be meaningful to all those involved.

The transition from woman to grandmother is another which needs celebration. When women and the feminine side are valued, the grandmother represents the wisest of persons, a woman who holds her blood, her power, and uses it to nurture and protect all the children and all the beings in the Circle of life. As she enters Moonpause, or menopause, she is finished with the raising of her own children and becomes a teacher of the women's traditions. In many tribal communities there was a Grandmothers council. In some cases, these grandmothers appointed the chiefs and removed them if they were not keeping the interest of all the people in their hearts as they made decisions. In others, this group of women had veto power on any action decided by the elder men's council. Their role was one of seeing that all the people were served by the leaders and the decisions they made. Brooke Medicine Eagle has referred to this group of women as the Grandmother Lodge and the transition ritual as induction into the Grandmother Lodge.[6] Women who are menopausal or who are not cycling for reasons of surgery can be inducted into the Grandmother Lodge. Again the rituals should be meaningful to the women involved, but I will share some of the rituals used in Grandmother Lodge ceremonies in which I have participated.

Setting of the sacred Circle and cleansing the space is the usual beginning. Songs and dancing, perhaps honoring the grandmothers and wise women teachers in our lives, are good to include. One ritual is the washing of the elder woman's feet or, if it seems right and you have a stream nearby, several women can take the initiate to the stream and undress her as much as she is comfortable with and bathe her. She can then be dressed in new clothing by her attendants and flowers placed in her hair. She is then brought back to the Circle where she might be anointed with a fragrant oil on her forehead, heart and belly. Each woman can then gift her with words describing her qualities which will serve her well as a Grandmother.

The initiate might make a commitment to nurture and renew all of life and to use her wisdom for the good of all. She might also be presented with a sash either red or black as a symbol of holding her power. I like red as a symbol of holding her blood, although black is the traditional color of the wise woman (red for the childbearing years, and white for the maiden). This sash may have been decorated by the women of the group or it may be left for the initiate to decorate with her own symbols of power. At this point, the new Grandmother may dance by herself or with other new Grandmothers. They are then asked to share some of their wisdom with the other women in the Circle. A final prayer for their strength and wisdom can be followed by a sharing of food and social time. This can be a very powerful ceremony for focusing the energy of the Moonpause woman in a positive way. The Grandmother can then continue to participate in the Moon Lodge Circle and, if there are enough grandmothers, a Grandmother Lodge may be formed as well. My experience has been that having Grandmothers as part of the Moon Lodge Circle is wonderful, as their wisdom and teaching is often needed.

Rites of birth and death can also be celebrated by the Moon Lodge in ways that are especially meaningful to the women. Birth might involve both welcoming the newborn into this life and supporting the new mother. My vision of the birth of my grandchildren is one where my women friends and I attend the birth with drums to welcome the new babe with the sound of the heart beat and singing, and provide the support for the mother that only a Circle of women can bring. I have no grandchildren yet, but I am waiting for the opportunity.

Death is another transition to a new beginning. It is unfortunate that we find it so difficult to talk to the dying about death. A dying person can use rituals in preparation for the transition. Creating a ritual after death is both a celebration of the person's life as lived and a releasing of that person's spirit to the new beginnings.

Rites of passage facilitate the transitions in our lives and help us to stay focused while many changes are taking place in our bodies and whole beings. They provide recognition of the journey and support for the process, and they continue to remind us of our travels around the great Wheel of Life.

Rites of Cycle

We have already mentioned rituals which might accompany the passing of the seasons—Spring Equinox for new growth; Summer Solstice for the sun, joy, and flowering; Fall Equinox for bringing things to closure, bearing fruit, harvest; Winter Solstice for seeds waiting to grow, welcoming the sun in its journey back. Along with these are ceremonies to celebrate the bounty of the Earth, the rain, the sun, the trees, the flowers.

The cycle transitions within our own lives might also be honored alone or within the Circle—marriage, divorce, children, achievement. We can also acknowledge inner work well done, acts of power and beauty completed.

The Moon rites are those which surround our Moon cycle and can be done alone or within the Moon Lodge. One of the things you can do when you take time to be alone during Moontime is to create a ritual to honor yourself as a woman. Creating an altar, using a special cloth with symbols important to you on it along

157

with flowers and perhaps a candle or incense is a good way to begin. Your ritual might include drumming, singing, or dancing. Doing craft work during Moontime can also be a ritual. With every bead, stitch or part put in place, a prayer or affirmation might be said. The result is a very power filled object. Using your Moon blood in a ritual way to feed and nourish your plants or garden, or even just giving it back to the Earth is also very empowering. There are many ways to collect your blood. Placing tampons, pads, or sponges in a jar or bowl of cold water and rinsing them out is an easy way. The Menstrual Wealth Catalog carries cloth pads and a Moon bowl to soak them in. Putting on a skirt and going out to sit on some moss to bleed directly onto the Earth is also a powerful experience. Moon blood can also be used as paint for shields or other ceremonial objects which you might make. The process of using your blood in a sacred way also serves to reshape the negative view of it which living in this culture imparts. It is not dirty, smelly, or polluting, as patriarchal society and the feminine hygiene companies would have us believe. Working with it, using it in a sacred way, and honoring it will help you to get in touch with its power.

Rituals for a Moon Lodge Circle are also those which honor the cycle of life and womanhood. Often just observing the rule that elders go first because of their wisdom is a good ritual that helps us tune into the cycle of life. Elders talk first, eat first, etc. and ceremonies might be done in a Circle ordered by age. A beautiful closing ritual was used by a group of women who met for ten days in support of a vision quest. The eldest woman present washed the feet of the next eldest while sharing her wisdom for the younger woman's continued growth, this continued down the line until the youngest washed the feet of the eldest, completing the cycle and indicating that even the youngest have wisdom to share. Foot washing and anointing with fragrant oil is a symbol of nurturing and support of each other. Group meditation, either guided or to drumming, is excellent as are healing Circles. When we focus our energy and intention together, healing energy can be directed to others, through our hands, our hearts, and even sent across space to affect those not present. Once the energy of the group is raised through meditation, drumming, and intent, it can then be focused and sent forth as needed. This is an experience difficult to describe in words and needs to be experienced to be appreciated. Dancing and connecting yourselves to the Earth through your feet, singing, drumming, using rattles, all allow our spirits to feel the connection to each other and the Circle of life. Your Circle might also make power objects which represent your growth process—shields, rattles, masks, drums, sculpture, bead work, weaving—and dance them awake in a ritual. A Circle I am involved with had an overnight in which we created an altar in the center of the room and all slept with our heads toward the center after drinking a wonderful herbal tea to enhance dreaming. Full and new Moon celebrations are always fun. You can make a full Moon tea by letting a jar of herbs and water sit in the light of the full Moon, and drink it as part of your celebration. Full Moon celebrations honor the time of ovulation and are very energetic, a good time for some wild dancing. New Moon celebrations are usually quieter and more meditative, honoring Moontime and cleansing. Women often create rituals which both meet their needs and create oneness within the Circle . Some women have a ritual of going around the Circle with the talking stick once when they first gather to allow each woman to state anything on her mind that she needs to express or release. This is a different kind of cleansing. Other women set specific meetings where only drumming, music making and dancing take place, with no talking.

As we come together in our beauty as women, we can begin to see our own beauty and power reflected in each other. This is an exciting and wonderful process which I believe we each hunger for at the depths of our souls. Create a ritual to break through the fear that keeps you from this sacred connection.

10

Women as Warriors

The Spiral Dance

"So, how are you feeling now? Have you had a chance to process your initiation into the Moon Lodge?"

"Well, there are so many feelings I have about it, I don't know quite where to start."

"Just start anywhere you like and we will let it circle in any direction you feel like going with it."

"First, I guess I would like to talk about how I felt with my bleeding arriving. I was so excited that my moon had come at last. I ran to tell mom and she was excited too. She told me the story of her first Moontime and I really felt that we were sharing something from woman to woman, like I wasn't a child anymore. It felt both wonderful and scary at the same time. Then she told me that I should find a place to be alone until suppertime. I asked her if it was ok to go to the clearing in the woods, the Moon Circle. She said that would be a perfect place. I she gave me a blanket and some juice and fruit and she said she'd come for me there later.

"It was so peaceful there. I lay on mother Earth with my belly pressed against hers and I felt a connection to all the women who had come there to bleed. I bathed in the pools, swimming with the trout and then laid in the sun to dry. I felt so safe there, so nurtured by the beauty around me. When I felt cramps, I did some of the exercises you showed me and sat like the frog taught us to sit. I felt very special being there.

"Then Mother came and I was so surprised to see all the women of the Moon Lodge and the Grandmother Lodge behind her. The wreath of flowers you put on my head made me feel so special. And when I stood in the Circle while you all sang to me, each speaking about the gifts you feel I have to give and giving me a gift to remind me of them. When you marked my face with red Earth paint as one who bleeds but does not die I truly felt that my Moon was a mysterious gift from the Creator. Walking back home through the woods in the dark, I felt I was the richest person in the world."

"We all felt rich welcoming you into our Circle."

"That night I had a dream. I was dancing as I danced that night in the Circle but this time I was part of a spiral of women. The center of the spiral was the time of creation and this spiral was made up of women holding hands through time and dancing. I was the last to join, so I was at the end, but I could see others coming to join the dance. We were all wearing red sashes even though we were dressed in many different ways. The red sash was like part of a uniform, it was one thing we all had in common. We were dancing in rhythm with the heartbeat of Mother Earth while Grandmother Moon beamed brightly above. We were dancing and singing and the sound was so beautiful. So many voices in harmony. I woke up smiling and the image of the dance stays with me even now. I went to the Moon Lodge and wrote the dream into the dream journal. It was even more powerful when I looked through the dreams of other women over time only to discover that they had similar dreams. Isn't that incredible?"

"Women's blood mysteries are always incredible. It is more than our bleeding that links us all together in this lodge today. It is also the commitment to use our power well, to always be our highest and finest selves, to create beauty, to claim the soft power. This means that we use our gifts and talents to nurture all of life, to better our community, to protect the children and respect the elders. While in our everyday work women and men share nearly all tasks, our experience is often different, and we contribute the products of our uniqueness to the community. You are now officially walking the path of the warrior woman. She is as passionate about her own growth as she is about fulfilling her role as a woman and contributing her own unique gifts to the community. Your woman name which was given to you in the ceremony speaks to that work."

"I can't believe that I have such a beautiful name. I hope some day that the inner beauty I have found and the outer beauty I have created will be worthy of such a name."

"It will, Brings the Dawn's Light."

Sisters of the Moon
Drums again are beating
Hearts again are meeting
Together around our Moon.[1]

Where Is the War?

Saying that women are warriors implies that there is some kind of war going on. It is a war going on many levels, but not the kind of war that we see in the world today. It is a war to reclaim lost territory and that territory exists within us, between us, and around us. Being a warrior means that we recognize the enemy that lives within and are committed to freeing our spirits and claiming the feminine values for ourselves and our world. Being a warrior means facing the death of our former selves as we grow in beauty. It means fighting for the children, that they may grow up with love and nurturing. The battlefield is anywhere and everywhere we find lack of value for the feminine or our children—in ourselves, in our homes, in our communities, in our country, all over the Earth.

Most of us already know well the battle that is taking place within us. The battle between what we know to be true and what society expects of us. To let the truth win, we must often stand alone on the battlefield and face the multitudes surrounding us. The most powerful weapon we have is our truth and our love, so standing in our center we speak our truth with love and we survive. It seems odd to be talking about these things in the language of war, but it is a familiar language to us and there is a need to reinterpret the language in a more positive and productive way. If we understand that the conflicts which occur in the outer world are reflections of the conflicts in our inner worlds, we can understand better where the battles must first be fought. I recall a time a number of years ago when I was upset with all the pollution and destruction of our natural resources. I was upset with our country, the government, "the other"—things outside of me. Since then I have seen how my choices moment to moment throughout my day—of what I eat, of what I buy, of what I use, of what I do—create this pollution and destruction. If it does not change within me, it cannot change in the larger world. Peace begins within your one heart, not in some treaty signed by men. Thus, the war is really inside.

When I first realized this, it was not what I wanted to know. It would be so much easier if someone else could negotiate the peace and I could just benefit from it. It would be so much easier if someone else could take care of the pollution problem and I could just keep doing the stuff I always do. It seemed too hard to deal with all the stuff inside, the stuff I like to pretend isn't there and avoid working on. After all, it didn't seem like anyone else was having to do this hard work. Maybe it would be better to not know that the war is inside and not outside. But once you know, you cannot go back to the state of not knowing. The path becomes clearer and you know you must walk it. Warrior training begins.

Warrior Training

The first lesson of the warrior is about the soft power. This is a power which comes first from learning to stand in the center of your own Circle and from that position, understand the interconnection and interdependence of all things. Soft power is standing in your own truth with gentleness. There is a wonderful story in the *Medicine Cards* book about how the deer teaches us the power of gentleness.[2] The fawn is on its way up the sacred mountain and finds an ogre blocking the path. The ogre represents everyone's worst fears and demons. The fawn looks at the ogre with love and says gently, "Please let me pass. I'm on my way to see the Great Spirit." The ogre is so overcome by the fawn's love and compassion that he melts away.

The use of soft power recognizes that the demons we face have been wounded. We all carry the wounds of our childhood and the unbalanced culture in which we live. We need to be compassionate with others as we are compassionate with ourselves. We are all on the same side in this war, shedding the light of love on the demons who live within.

Soft power takes much more courage than tough power and power over. When you use power over in an aggressive way you do not have to do the work to stand in the center of your Circle. It allows you to distance yourself from others so you cannot see their wounding which reflects your own wounds. Aggressive power takes very little courage compared to soft power because you do not have to look at yourself. Soft power requires you to see yourself, love yourself, and offer that sight and love to others. Soft in our language often suggests a push-over, someone who is easy to control. Soft as we use it here refers to a value of treating others in a loving way. If you are moving from your center, you are certainly not pushed over very easily. You are in the warrior's stance with the energy of the universe moving through you. A woman warrior knows herself to be the center of the universe and therefore has the courage to take exquisite care of herself. A woman warrior knows herself to be the womb of creation and therefore has the love to take exquisite care of herself.

Taking care of yourself, physically, emotionally and spiritually is crucial to being able to standing your center. We are not perfect at this and thus are not in our center at all times. But if we work at the lessons which move us from our center, we are never too far way and we know the way back. To be centered at all times means we have no more lessons to learn, and I don't know anyone who has arrived at that point. So to use soft power we must come from the place of truth in our center, the place where love and connectedness reside.

When using soft power you simply stand strong in your center and allow your opponent to see the reflection of his or her lesson. It is like judo, where the energy of the opponent is used to throw the opponent, except it is done in a loving way. Translated into the language of assertiveness, it is speaking what is true for you in a gentle and loving voice and then following through with appropriate action. Soft power does not mean you need to put up with abusive behavior from others because you care for them. It means you speak out about the abuse to the person in a loving way and if it does not stop, you take whatever non-aggressive action is necessary to stop it—leave, call the police, whatever it takes. The warrior woman speaks and acts.

Another reason for referring to women as warriors is to help us to see women as strong. I find that women and men tend not to identify with the feminine side because they see it as weak. Let's change that image of women as weak to women as strong, but in a different way than men are strong. We are not talking about physical strength. This strength comes from the strength of conviction, our strength of knowing, the strength of our emotion, and the strength of our interconnection. We are strong like Grandmother Moon who pulls us into her mystery each month. We are strong like Mother Earth with our ability to bring forth new life. We are strong as we stand our ground, in Circle, for the nurturing of all things.

Another part of warrior training is understanding the process of community decision making. The hierarchical structure of our society and its institutions does not fit the feminine style. That type of structure is based on power over and competition. In the feminine style, diversity is honored and all have an equal voice within the Circle. The assumption is that each individual's needs will be taken into account along with the good of the whole group. Consensus decision making is a process which has its roots in tribal groups. It is quite different from the democratic process because there is not a majority or a minority. Instead there are individuals and the group. Every individual must agree to the action taken or decision made. It may take a long time to come to consensus, with each individual being heard many times. In larger communities there may be spokespersons representing different groups, but the rule that everyone must agree is upheld and the spokespersons represent the views of each individual in their groups. I recall that even as a teenager I was very fed up with the inequities created by a democratic system. I wrote this poem as an expression of my feeling.

One

When 50 million people laugh and smile without
    trying,
When 50 million people laugh, one is crying.
When 50 million people dine, eat their cookies, sip
    their tea,
When 50 million people dine, one is hungry.
When 50 million people sleep in blanketed bed which
    heat does hold,
When 50 million people sleep, one is cold.
When one in 50 million needs, the cries fall deaf on
    ears of fools, Who watch the one fall onto knees and
    cry "Majority rules."

Although I knew what I didn't like about the system, I did not yet know what could replace it. While consensus decision making is more cumbersome on a very large scale, if the foundations of our communities were based in this process we might not need such large-scale decision making. The Iroquois people have successfully used this process since the beginning of their Confederacy, both within their individual communities and in the larger meetings of the six nations involved. We are certainly not skilled in this process, but we can learn it and fine-tune it to our needs. Consensus decision making is important to the warrior woman because she knows what happens to each individual also affects her. If one is crying, then part of her is crying. This is the knowledge of our interconnection with all of life and we must find ways to honor that oneness.

The warrior understands herself to be a whole song, composed of physical, emotional, mental and spiritual notes. And so she realizes that she must work on many levels. It is not enough to bind the physical wound of the child. The emotional needs of the child must be tended to and the spirit of the child must be seen and connected with. It is not enough to harvest the food from your garden. The plant spirits and the emotion they have integrated must be honored. With everything we do in every moment of our lives, we can strive to meet the challenges as whole beings and see the wholeness of others as well.

Power resides in words. When we say a word we create a vibration which moves out into the universe and adds to the total vibration. The warrior chooses her words very carefully, as she knows she is creating a powerful vibration. The words that we speak help create our reality. If we speak words of peace and love, we help create a peaceful and loving world. When we sing of beauty, we help create that beauty in our daily lives.

Thought forms are also vibrations which filter out into the universe, though not quite as directly as words. Thoughts have consequences for our emotions and inner world. If we think angry thoughts, we become more angry. If we think sad thoughts, we become sadder. If we think fearful thoughts, we become more fearful. If we think peaceful thoughts, we become more peaceful. If we think joyful thoughts, we become more joyful. The warrior woman understands the relationship between her thoughts and emotions and seeks to gain control of her thoughts through inner work. I believe that somewhere there is a world where thoughts immediately manifest into action. None of us is ready to live in that world because we would probably self destruct within the first five minutes. Yet the warrior seeks inner harmony which must include the mind and thoughts. Angry, sad and fearful thoughts are transformed into teachers and lessons are learned. Joyful, peaceful and loving thoughts are cultivated like a garden of flowers.

Warrior training is really a re-claiming of the feminine values of nurturing, connection, and wholeness. Our blood is a symbol of these values as it nurtures new life, connects us to the whole Circle of Life, and calls us to wholeness through our Moontime rites.

Standing Alone and Standing Together

While we must stand in the center of our own Circle and stand there alone, we are also part of larger Circles. We are standing in Circle with all those who went before us, all women over time. There is the cave woman, counting days by marking them on a bone, as she cycles with the moon. There are women who enjoyed their position of value within their communities. There are women who were persecuted for healing with herbs, they were called witches and burned. There are women who were writers, artists, builders, leaders, mothers, doctors, and all else they might have aspired to be. We stand with these women and honor the wisdom their lives bring to us.

We also stand with the women of today. All of them. It doesn't matter whether they are mothers, doctors, teachers, factory workers, lawyers, street people or farmers. We are connected to them through our blood. What happens to them affects us. We feel their joy and their pain. They are dancing with us in this Circle and we see their wholeness as our own.

We stand with the women of tomorrow, those women yet to arrive. As warriors we know both our history and our future, but we live in the present. For what we do now creates the future for our daughters and granddaughters and great-granddaughters. How we speak, how we walk, how we move through our lives creates the world in which they will live. As we become warriors and learn to stand in our own Circle, we do it not just for ourselves, but for our sisters and brothers who are here now and for all those yet to come. We do this as well for the whole Circle of Life, for even the smallest blade of grass or pebble on the beach will feel the peace we create.

As we stand together we see the richness of our differences and feel the power of our sameness. Embracing the difference in our Circle is perhaps the greatest challenge for the warrior, for she is doing battle not just for those who support her but for those who have abused her as well. In a very powerful lesson, a teacher of mine simply said, "If you turn away from one woman, you turn away from them all." As we look beyond actions to see spirit in each living thing and to see our connection, perhaps it will be easier to see the importance of diversity.

Re-Claiming

Re-claiming means taking back that which was once ours. This book is about taking back our blood, our bodies, our wisdom and our value. This is the turf on which the warrior battles. Taking back our blood means honoring our cycles and using them as the tool of transformation in our lives. We are taking it back from the hands of patriarchy where it has been hidden and feared, and treated as a physical ailment. Women have menstruated since the beginning of time and men have always been in awe of she who bleeds but does not die. Only recently have men had dominion over women's menstrual rites. We must take back those rights and rites.

Taking back our bodies extends the battle to the medicalization of all women's natural functions. Birthing, menstruation, menopause, emotions, even death. We have been drugged and made to believe that the natural functions of our bodies are bad and need to be regulated to be acceptable. We now say that this is not our truth. We are finding our truth and it says that our natural functions are important sources of wisdom for us. They are not to be suppressed and artificially regulated. Only from a holistic approach which honors the physical, emotional and spiritual can we facilitate healing. We take back control of our bodies.

The wisdom of women lives inside, not in a book. We know what we know to be true and do not need an external source to validate it. This type of knowing is not seen as being as important as scientific knowledge. Our wisdom tells us that both are important and that without inner wisdom we cannot be whole. My vegetable garden grows in concentric circles. I know that my plants like it that way and they grow better. Is that an acceptable reason? Not to a scientist. Scientists can tell us many things about plants but they cannot tell us what plants like because the do not research the spirit of the plant. My wisdom comes from my connection to the spirit of the plants and thus I have a different kind of knowledge which is equally important. Our wisdom and intuitive knowing have been laughed at and degraded. We take back our wisdom and stand as warriors in our knowing.

Perhaps the most important reclamation that the woman warrior seeks is value. It permeates all the other areas we have talked about. Our struggles as women to achieve equality have come far, yet achieving equal value as women has lagged behind. We have earned the right to act like men but we are not yet valued as women. It is good that we can be like men if we choose; it would be better if they could be like us if they choose. We choose to be like men because what they do is valued. They choose not to be like us because what we do is not. There are many more similarities than differences between women and men, but the differences are very important and the ways in which we are different need to be valued. Value here means that feminine values, women's cycles, and women's wisdom is seen as necessary to the welfare of our communities and world. We re-claim our value as women.

May our swords be made of love and light.
May our words be chosen with wisdom.
May our thoughts bring peace.
May we sing and dance our beauty
May our blood renew the Earth.

Notes

Chapter 1

1. Sue Kalchik St. Pierre "A New Moon Is Rising," from *Out of the Womb Singing Sweetly*. Audiotape, 1991. (Available from the Ladyslipper Catalogue.)

2. Barbara Walker. *The Women's Encyclopedia of Myths and Secrets*. New York: Harper Collins, 1983.

3. Ibid.

4. S.H. Hooke. *Middle Eastern Mythology*. Harmondsworth, England: Penguin Books, 1963.

5. T. Gaster. Myth, *Legend and Custom in the Old Testament*. New York: Harper & Row, 1969.

6. Walker, op cit.

7. E. Showalter. *The Female Malady: Women, Madness, and English Culture, 1830-1980*. New York: Pantheon, 1987

8. Quoted in Sophie Laws, Valerie Hey, and Andrea Egan. *Seeing Red*. London: Hutchinson and Co. Ltd., 1985.

9. R. Norris and C. Sullivan. *PMS*. New York: Rawson Associates, 1983.

10. R. F. Casper and M. T. Hearn. "The Effect of Hysterectomy and Bilateral Oophorectamy in Women with Severe Premenstrual Syndrome." *American Journal of Obstretics and Gynecology*, 162: 105-109, 1990.

11. Thomas Buckley and Alma Gottlieb. *Blood Magic: The Anthropology of Menstruation*. Berkeley: University of California Press, 1988.

12. Rhoda Unger and Mary Crawford. *Women and Gender: A Feminist Psychology*. New York: McGraw-Hill, Inc., 1992.

13. Ibid.

14. Brooke Medicine Eagle. *Buffalo Woman Comes Singing*. New York: Ballantine Books, 1991

15. T. J. Cloudsley. *Rhythmic Activity in Animal Physiology and Behavior*. New York: Academic Press, 1961; E. M. Dewan, M. F. Medkin and J. Rock. "Effect of photic stimulation on the human menstrual cycle." *Photochemistry and Photobiology*, 27: 581-585, 1978; C. Hauenschild. "Lunar periodicity." *Cold Spring Harbor Symposium on Quantitative Biology*, 25: 491-497, 1960; W. Menaker and A. Menaker. "Lunar periodicity in human reproduction: A likely unit of biological time." *American Journal of Obstetrics and Gynaecology*, 77: 905-914, 1959.

16. Buckley and Gottlieb, op cit.

17. Medicine Eagle, op cit.

18. Ruby Modesto and Guy Mount. *Not for Innocent Ears*. Arcata, CA: Sweetlight Books, 1980

19. Buckley and Gottlieb, op cit.

20. Joyce C. Mills. "Premenstrual Syndrome: Symptom, or Source of Transformation?" *Psychological Perspectives*, 19:1, 101-110, 1988.

21. Ibid.

22. Alma Gottlieb. "Menstrual cosmology among the Beng of Ivory Coast." In *Buckley and Gottlieb*, op cit.

23. Chris Knight. "Menstrual Synchrony and the Australian rainbow snake." In *Buckley and Gottlieb*, op cit.

24. Medicine Eagle, op cit.

25. Janice Delaney, Mary Jane Lupton, and Emily Toth. *The Curse*. New York: E.P. Dutton and Co., Inc., 1987.

26. J. Rierdan. "Variations in the Experience of Menarche as a Function of Preparedness." In S. Golub, ed., *Menarche: The Transition from Girl to Woman*. Lexington, MA: Lexington Books, 1983.

27. J. Brooks-Gunn and D. N. Ruble. "Dysmenorrhea in Adolescence." In *S. Golub*, op cit.

28. Medicine Eagle, op cit.

29. Sandra L. Bem. "The Measurement of Psychological Androgyny." *Journal of Consulting and Clinical Psychology* 42: 155-162. 1974.

30. E. P. Cook. *Psychological Androgyny*. New York: Pergamon, 1985.

31. Mills, op cit.

Chapter 2

1. "Spirit of the Wind." Written by Star Williams and recorded by Brooke Medicine Eagle on *A Gift of Song*. Audiotape, 1989. Available from Harmony Network, P.O. Box 2550, Guerneville, CA 95446. Every attempt was made to locate the author for permission but we were not able to find Ms. Williams.

2. Anne Moir and David Jessel. *Brain Sex: The Real Difference between Men and Women*. New York: Carol Publishing Group, 1991.

3. E. J. Mackenberg, D. M. Broverman, W. Vogel, and E. L. Klaiber. "Morning-to-Afternoon Changes in Cognitive Performances and in the Electroencephalogram." *Journal of Educational Psychology*, 6, 1974.

4. D. M. Broverman, W. Vogel, E. L. Klaiber, D. Majcher, D. Shea, and V. Paul. "Changes in Cognitive Task Performance across the Menstrual Cycle." *Journal of Comparative and Physiological Psychology*, 95:4, 1981.

5. Buckley and Gottlieb, *Blood Magic*, op cit.

6. Margaret Henderson. "Evidence for Hormonally Related Male Temperature Cycle and Synchrony with the Female Cycle." *Australian and New Zealand Journal of Medicine*, 6:254, 1976.

7. D. Sanders, P. Warner, T. Backstrom, and J. Bancroft. "Mood, Sexuality, Hormones, and the Menstrual Cycle." *Psychosomatic Research*, 45:487-501, 1983.

8. Charles Debrovner, ed. *Premenstrual Tension: A Multidisciplinary Approach*. Human Sciences Press, 1982 .

9. J.M. Steil and B. A. Turelsky. "Is Equal Better? The Relationship between Marital Equality and Psychological Symptomatology. In S. Oskamp, ed., *Family Processes and Problems: Social Psychological Aspects*. Bevery Hills, CA: Sage Publications, 1987.

10. J. M. Steil and K. Weltman. "Marital Inequality: The Importance of Resources, Personal Attributes, and Social Norms on Career Valuing and the Allocation of Domestic Responsibilities." *Sex Roles*, 24:161-179, 1991.

11. Alice J. Dan. "The Law and Women's Bodies: The Case of Menstruation Leave in Japan." In Virginia L. Olesen and Nancy Fugate Woods, eds., *Culture, Society, and Menstruation*. Washington: Hemisphere Publishing Corp., 1986.

12. Brooke Medicine Eagle, Lecture at "Deeping of Spirit" camp, 1989.

13. Ibid.

14. Barbara Walker (1983). *The Women's Ecyclopedia of Myths and Secrets*. NewYork: Harper Collins, 1993.

15. Penelope Shuttle and Peter Redgrove. *The Wise Wound*. New York: Richard Marek, 1978.

16. Emily Martin. "Premenstrual Syndrome: Discipline, Work, and Anger in Late Industrial Societies." In Buckley and Gottlieb, *Blood Magic*.

Chapter 3

1. Linda Heron Wind. "Balsam Flower Song." 1991.

2. Herbert Benson. *Beyond the Relaxation Response.* New York: Times Books, 1984.

3. Ibid.

4. Irene L. Goodale, Alice D. Domar, and Herbert Benson. "Alleviation of Premenstrual Syndrome Symptoms with the Relaxation Response." *Obstetrics and Gynecology,* 75:4, 649-655, 1990.

5. An excellent drumming tape is Brooke Medicine Eagle's "Drumming the Heartbeat," available from Harmony Network, P.O. Box 2550, Guerneville, CA 95446.

6. Stephen Eligio Gallegos. *The Personal Totem Pole: Animal Imagery, the Chakras, and Psychotherapy.* Santa Fe, NM: Moon Bear Press, 1987.

7. Becca Zinn. Stardust: *The Musings of a Gradually Awakeing Soul.* Kansas City, MO: Uni Sun/Stillpoint, 1986.

8. Clarissa Pinkola Estes. *Women Who Run with the Wolves: Myths and Stories of the Wild Woman Archetype.* New York: Ballantine Books, 1992.

9. Jamie Sams and David Carson. *Medicine Cards.* Santa Fe, NM: Bear and Company, 1988.

10. Marie-Lu Lorler. *Shamanic Healing within the Medicine Wheel.* Albuquerque, NM: Brotherhood of Life, 1989; Sun Bear and Wabun. *The Medicine Wheel: Earth Astrology.* New York: Prentice Hall Press, 1980; Brooke Medicine Eagle. *Buffalo Woman Comes Singing.*

Chapter 4

1. Rashani. "Pueo." Recorded on *Keeper of the Mysteries,* 1988. Audiotape available from Medicine Song Productions, 2015 Menalto Ave., Menlo Park, CA 94025.

2. Hilary C. Maddux. *Menstruation.* New Canaan, CN: Tokey Publishing Co., 1975.

3. Dena Taylor. *Red Flower: Rethinking Menstruation.* Freedom, CA: The Crossing Press, 1988.

4. Shuttle and Redgrove. *The Wise Wound.*

5. Marilyn Nagy. "Menstruation and Shamanism." In Louise Mahdi, Steven Foster, and Meredith Little, eds. *Betwixt and Between: Patterns of Masculine and Feminine Initiation.* La Salle, IL: Open Court Publishers, 1987.

6. Ibid.

7. Robert. L. Van De Castle. *The Psychology of Dreaming* (pamphlet). New York: General Learning Press, 1971.

8. Evelyn Reynolds. "Variations of Mood and Recall in the Menstrual Cycle." *Journal of Psychosomatic Research*, 13: 163-166 1969.

9. Ernest Hartman. *The Biology of Dreaming.* Springfield, IL: Charles C. Thomas, 1967.

10. Brooke Medicine Eagle. "Women's Moon Time: A Call to Power." *Shaman's Drum*, Spring, 21, 1986.

11. Mary Dillon. *Flowering Woman: Moontime for Kory.* Sedona, Arizona: Sunlight Productions, 1988.

12. Taylor, *Red Flower.*

13. Marion Woodman. *Leaving My Father's House: A Journey to Conscious Femininity.* Boston: Shambhala, 1993.

14. Estes, *Women Who Run with the Wolves.*

15. Clarissa Pinkola Estes. *In the House of the Riddle Mother.* Audiotape, 1991. Available from Sounds True Recordings, 735 Walnut St., Boulder, CO 80302.

16. Marion Woodman. *Dreams: Language of the Soul.* Audiotape, 1992. Available from Sounds True Recordings.

17. Patricia Garfield. *Women's Bodies, Women's Dreams.* New York: Ballantine Books, 1988.

Chapter 5

1. Ani Williams. "She." Music by Ani Williams, lyrics adapted from poem "Keeping Time" by Will Ashe Bason. *Recorded on Children of the Sun.* Audiotape, 1992. Available from Earthsong Productions, 2675 W. HWY. 89A, Suite 1091, Sedona, AZ 86336. (602)282-7053.

2. Medicine Eagle. *Buffalo Woman Comes Singing.*

3. Brooke Medicine Eagle. *Moon Time.* Audiotape, 1987. Available from Harmony Network, P.O. Box 2550, Guerneville, CA 95446.

Chapter 6

1. Elaine Peterson, "Moon Song." A version recorded on Brooke Medicine Eagle, *Visions Speaking.* Audiotape, 1991. Available from Harmony Network, P.O. Box 2550, Guerneville, CA 95446.

2. Dana C. Jack. *Silencing the Self: Women and Depression.* Cambridge, MA: Harvard University Press, 1991.

3. Emily Martin, "Premenstrual Syndrome," op cit.

4. Sue Kalchik St. Pierre. "Our Sacred Tears," from *Out of the Womb Singing Sweetly.*

5. "Ancient Mother." I have been unable to locate the original author of this song; it has become a traditional song for many women's gatherings.

Chapter 7

1. Marcia Meuse. "Vision Beauty Song." Recorded on Brooke Medicine Eagle, *Visions Speaking*. Audiotape, 1991. Available from Harmony Network, P.O. Box 2550, Guerneville, CA 95446.

2. John Robbins. *Diet for a New America*. Walpole, NH: Stillpoint. 1988.

3. Linda Ojeda. *Exclusively Female: A Nutritional Guide for Better Menstrual Health*. Claremont, CA: Hunter House, 1983.

4. Ibid.

5. Ibid.

6. Ibid.

7. Rosemary Gladstar. *Herbal Healing for Women*. New York: Fireside — Simon & Shuster., 1993.

8. Jack Tips. *Pro Vita Plan*. Austin, TX: Apple-A-Day Press, 1992.

9. Gladstar. *Herbal Healing for Women*.

10. Jeannine Parvati Hygieia. *A Woman's Herbal*. Wildwood House, 1978.

11. Susun Weed. *Wise Woman Herbal for the Childbearing Years*. Woodstock, NY: Ash Tree Publishing, 1986.

12. Gladstar. *Herbal Healing for Women*.

13. Stella Weller. *Pain-free Periods: Natural Ways to Overcome Menstrual Problems*. Rochester, VT: Thorsons Publishers, Inc., 1987.

14. Ibid.

15. Patricia Nell Warren. *One is the Sun*. New York: Ballantine Books, 1991, p. 345-348.

Chapter 8

1. Brooke Medicine Eagle. "I Walk a Path of Beauty." From *Visions Speaking*. Audiotape, 1991. Available from Harmony Network.

2. Medicine Eagle, *Buffalo Woman Comes Singing*.

Chapter 9

1. Brooke Medicine Eagle. "I Give Away this Blood of Life." From *A Gift of Song*.

2. Brooke Medicine Eagle. *Healing through Ritual Action*. Audiotape, 1986. Available from Harmony Network.

3. Mary Dillon. *Flowering Woman*.

4. Alexandra Kolkmeyer. *The Clear Red Stone*. Santa Fe, NM: In Sight Press, 1983.

5. Naomi Ruth Lowinsky. *Stories from the Motherline: Reclaiming the Mother-Daughter Bond: Finding our Feminine Souls*. Los Angeles: Jeremy P. Tarcher, Inc., 1992.

6. Brooke Medicine Eagle. "Grandmother's Wisdom." Audiotape, 1993. Available from Harmony Network.

Chapter 10

1. Sue Kalchik St. Pierre. "Sisters of Our Moon," From *Out of the Womb Singing Sweetly*.

2. Sams and Carson. *Medicine Cards*.

Appendix A

DAILY RATING FORM

To use the daily rating form, at the end of each day, record the following:

1. Indicate the date.
2. Circle Y or N to indicate whether you were menstruating that day.
3. Indicate the phase of the moon on the appropriate dates, new moon, waxing, full moon, waning.
4. Record the number that best represents each of the characteristics listed.
5. If you have any further clarifying comments on any of the characteristics, write them on a separate page or in a journal.

	MON	TUE	WED	THU	FRI	SAT	SUN
DATE							
MENSTRUATING? (Y or N)							
MOON PHASE (N,Wax, F, Wan)							

RATE BELOW FROM 1 - 6

Irritable, angry, impatient							
Eat more, crave foods							
Sleep more, naps							
Low Energy, tired, weak							
Depressed, sad, low, blue, tearful							
Sexual interest							
Desire to be alone							
Restless, can't sit still							
Headaches							
Anxious, jittery, nervous							
Increased efficiency							
Breast pain							
Creative, new ideas							
Back, joint or muscle pain							
Feel bloated, water retention							
Stay home, avoid social activity							
Feel less like working							
Abdominal pain							
Vivid dreams							
Mood swings							
Increased sense of well-being							
Low self-esteem							
Took time for yourself							
MADE JOURNAL ENTRY (Y or N)							

Rate each characteristic: 1=Not at all, 2=Minimal, 3=Mild, 4=Moderate, 5=A lot, 6=Extreme

Permission is granted to photocopy this page

Appendix B

Books on Menstruation

Thomas Buckley and Alma Gottlieb (1988). *Blood Magic: The Anthropology of Menstruation*. Berkley: University of Cal-ifornia Press.

Mary Daly (1978). *Gyn/ecology: The Metaethics of Radical Feminism*. Boston: Beacon Press.

Mary Dillon (1988). *Flowering Woman: Moontime for Kory: A Story of A Girl's Rites of Passage into Womanhood*. Sedona, AZ: Sunlight Productions.

Luisa Francia (1991). *Dragontime: Magic and Mystery of Menstruation*. Woodstock, NY: Ash Tree Publishing.

Demetra George (1992). *Mysteries of the Dark Moon: The Healing Power of the Dark Goddess*. Harper San Francisco.

Sharon Golub (1985). *Lifting the Curse of Menstruation: A Feminist Appraisal of the Influence of Menstruation on Women's Lives*. New York: The Haworth Press.

Sharon Golub (1992). *Periods: From Menarche to Menopause*. Newbury Park, CA: Sage Publications.

Chris Knight (1991). *Blood Relations: Menstruation and the Origins of Culture.* New Haven: Yale University Press.

Alexandra Kolkmeyer (1982). *The Clear Red Stone: A Myth and the Meaning of Menstruation.* Santa Fe: In Sight Press.

Vicki Noble (1991. *Shakti Woman: Feeling Our Fire, Healing Our World.* Harper San Francisco.

Lara Owen (1993). *Her Blood is Gold: Celebrating the Power of Menstruation.* Harper San Francisco.

Penelope Shuttle and Peter Redgrove (1988). *The Wise Wound: Myths, Realities, and Meanings of Menstruation.* New York: Bantam Books.

Tamara Slayton (1990). *Reclaiming the Menstrual Matrix: Evolving Feminine Wisdom - A Workbook.* Menstrual Health Foundation, P.O. Box 3248, Santa Rosa, California 95402.

Spider (1992). *Songs of Bleeding.* New York: Black Thistle Press.

Kisma K. Stepanich (1992). *Sister Moon Lodge: The Power and Mystery of Menstruation.* St. Paul MN: Llewellyn Publications.

Dena Taylor (1988). *Red Flower: Rethinking Menstruation.* Freedom, CA: The Crossing Press.

Stella Weller (1987). *Pain-free Periods: Natural Ways to Overcome Menstrual Problems.* Rochester, VT: Thorsons Publishers, Inc.

Other Books of Interest

Paula Gunn Allen (1987). *The Sacred Hoop: Recovering the Feminine in American Indian Traditions.* Boston: Beacon Press.

Sun Bear and Wabun (1991). *The Medicine Wheel: Earth Astrology.* New York: Prentice Hall Press.

Anne Cameron (1981). *Daughters of Copper Woman.* Vancouver: Press Gang.

Clarissa Pinkola Estes (1992). *Women Who Run with the Wolves: Myths and Stories of the Wild Woman Archetype.* New York: Ballantine Books.

Eligio Stephen Gallegos (1987). *The Personal Totem Pole: Animal Imagery, the Chakras, and Psychotherapy.* Santa Fe: Moon Bear Press.

Eligio Stephen Gallegos (1992). *Animals of the Four Windows: Integrating Thinking, Sensing, Feeling and Imagery.* Sante Fe: Moon Bear Press.

Patricia Garfield (1988). *Women's Bodies, Women's Dreams.* New York: Ballantine Books.

Marie-Lu Lorler (1989). *Shamanic Healing within the Medicine Wheel.* Albuquerque, NM: Brotherhood of Life.

Vicki Nobel (1983). *Motherpeace: A way to the Goddess through Myth, Art, and Tarot.* San Francisco: Harper and Row.

Jeannine Parvati (1978). *Hygieia, A Woman's Herbal* Wildwood House.

Jamie Sams (1990). *Sacred Path Cards: The Discovery of Self through Native Teachings.* Harper San Francisco.

Jamie Sams (1993) *The Thirteen Original Clan Mothers.* Harper San Francisco.

Jamie Sams and David Carson (1988). *Medicine Cards.* Santa Fe: Bear and Co.

Jamie Sams and Twylah Nitsch (1991). *Other Council Fires Were Here Before Ours.* Harper San Francisco.

Rosemary Gladstar (1993), *Herbal Healing for Women.* New York: Fireside — Simon & Shuster.

Starhawk (1989). *The Spiral Dance.* New York: Harper & Row.

Susun Weed (1986). *Wise Woman Herbal for the Childbearing Year.* Woodstock, NY: Ash Tree Publishing.

Susun Weed (1992). Wise Woman Ways — Menopausal Years. Woodstock, New York: Ash Tree Publishing.

185

Tapes

Songs and Chants

A Gift of Song, Visions Speaking, For My People, Singing Joy to the Earth, and *Drumming the Heartbeat* by Brooke Medicine Eagle. Available from Harmony Network, P.O. Box 2550, Guerneville, CA 95446.

Out of the Womb Singing Sweetly by Sue Kalchik St. Pierre. Available from the Ladyslipper Catalogue.

Keeper of the Mysteries by Rashani. Available from Medicine Song Productions, 2015 Menalto Ave, Menlo CA 94025.

Children of the Sun by Ani Williams and Mazatl Galindo. Available from Earthsong Productions, 2675 W. Hwy 89A, Suite 1091, Sedona, AZ 86336.

The Spirit Who Sings and *Return to Remember* by Andrea Lyman, Moonbear Productions, P.O. Box 135, Sagle, Idaho 83860.

Medicine Wheel by On Wings of Song and Robert Gass. Spring Hill Music, P.O. Box 800, Boulder, CO 80306

Come to the Circle by Joyful Noise Productions, P.O. Box 295, Norwich, VT 05055.

Teaching Tapes

Available from Harmony Network, by Brooke Medicine Eagle:

> *Moon Time*
> *Moon Lodge*
> *Healing through Ritual Action*
> *Visioning Part 1 and 2*
> *Empowering the Spiritual Warrior: Walking a Beauty Path*
> *Grandmother Wisdom: Lessons from the Moon-Pause Lodge*

Available from Sounds True Recordings, 735 Walnut St., Boulder, CO 80302:

Dreams: Language of the Soul by Marion Woodman

In the House of the Riddle Mother by Clarissa Pinkola Estes

Magic, Vision, and Action: Changing Consciousness,
   Healing the Earth by Starhawk

Available from L. Crow Enterprises, P.O. Box 11, Basin, MT 59631:

   Coming Home to Our North American Roots by Lynne
   Dusenberry Crow

Catalogs

Sounds True Recordings, 735 Walnut St., Boulder, CO 80302 (800-333-
   9185)

Menstrual Wealth Catalogue from New Cycle Products, P.O. Box 1775,
   Sebastopol, CA 95472 (800-845- FLOW or 707-829-2744)

Ladyslipper Catalog: Recordings by Women, P.O. Box 3124-R, Durham,
   NC 27715 (800-634-6044)

The sheet music for all the chants and songs featured in *New Moon Rising*
   are available for $4.00 plus $1.00 shipping and handling from Delphi
   Press, P.O. Box 267990, Chicago, IL 60626.

Linda Heron Wind is professor of Psychology at Nazareth College in Rochester, New York, She also has a small private practice in psychotherapy. In her therapeutic work she sees mostly women and employs a transpersonal approach in facilitating the process of growth and change. Dr. Wind has conducted women's therapy groups over a number of years and is part of an ongoing women's circle devoted to spiritual growth and development of community. For the last five years she has participated in vision quests and helped facilitate vision quest camps for women with Brooke Medicine Eagle in Montana.

The guiding vision of her life and work is to facilitate the process of healing the separation among the peoples of Earth, between women and men, between humans and nature, and between the physical and the spiritual, that we might all remember our oneness with all things.